Ros

Rose Oil

THE NEW GUIDE TO NATURE'S MOST PRECIOUS PERFUME AND TRADITIONAL REMEDY

Julia Lawless

Thorsons

An Imprint of HarperCollins*Publishers*

To 'Didi'

Thorsons
An Imprint of HarperCollins*Publishers*
77–85 Fulham Palace Road,
Hammersmith, London W6 8JB
1160 Battery Street,
San Francisco, California 94111-1213

Published by Thorsons 1995
10 9 8 7 6 5 4 3 2 1

A catalogue record for this book
is available from the British Library

ISBN 0 7225 3173 7

Printed in Great Britain by

Contents

ophthalmia; cuts and wounds; depression; dermatitis and eczema; dry/cracked skin; dysmenorrhoea (painful periods); faintness and dizziness; haemorrhoids; hangover; hay fever; headaches; heat rash; high blood-pressure; immune system (to strengthen); infectious illness; insomnia; leucorrhoea and pruritis; menopausal problems; menorrhagia (heavy periods); menstruation problems; migraine; mouth ulcers; palpitations; perfume uses; perspiration (excessive); pregnancy and childbirth; premenstrual tension (PMT); scars; sensitive skin; sexual problems; skin care; stress; thread veins; varicose veins

Acknowledgements

The title 'Queen of Flowers' was bestowed on the rose by the Greek poetess Sappho over 2,500 years ago. Since that time the rose has been transformed from a simple five-petalled blossom into a multitude of cultivated forms. Its role has also undergone a dramatic change: during the early history of its development it was grown principally for its medicinal properties and its perfume; today the rose is known mainly as a garden flower.

Yet there remains something quite unique and ageless about the appeal of a rose. Its perfect form and perfume seem to imbue it with an inner quality, and thus it has always held an honoured place in the imagination of humanity – a symbol of divinity and the transcendent nature of the soul. It is with this in mind and an awareness that the rose is the favoured flower of the Sufi tradition that this book is dedicated to my sister-in-law, Didi.

I would also like to thank the following people for

their help and assistance over the last few months: John Black for his expertise and for providing technical information; Cara Denman for her guidance; Jane Graham-Maw and those at Thorsons for their sympathetic approach; Len Smith for his editorial notes and advice; and last but not least, my husband Alec and daughter Natasha for their ongoing support.

Julia Lawless
October 1995

Rose Oil: An Introduction

Oh, no man knows
Through what wild centuries
Roves back the rose.

Walter de la Mare, *All That's Past*

When did the passion for the rose begin? Fossil studies have shown that wild roses were already blooming 40 million years ago! Simple rose images have been identified on murals and in sculptural relief forms dating from the earliest historical times. The oldest of these is depicted on the wall of the excavated Palace of Knossos in Crete, believed to be more than 4,000 years old. A rose is also stamped on one of the oldest coins which has been unearthed, a 2000 BC Hittite artefact. However, these ancient specimens are difficult to identify with botanical accuracy because of the basic nature of the design.

No such doubt exists, however, with respect to a wreath of five-petalled flowers which was discovered in an Egyptian tomb (circa AD 26) by British archaeologist Sir Flinders Petrie in 1888:

*In the dry desert air, the wreath's petals had shrivelled,
but they still kept their colour, and when placed in
warm water, the blossoms seemed to come back to life.
Buds swelled, and the pink petals spread, unfolding to
reveal the knot of golden threads at the centre just as
they must have been on the morning of the funeral. A
botanist at Cambridge had little trouble in identifying
Petrie's flowers as roses, specimens of 'Rosa richardii'
(R. sancta), a species already known as 'the Holy Rose
of Abyssinia' because at that time it was still a fixture
of the Coptic Christian churchyards in that country.*[1]

Similar remains have also been found in graves
throughout Middle Egypt, together with frescoes and
scraps of fabric portraying simple roses with five petals.
It is significant that the rose was one of the flowers
sacred to the Egyptian Goddess Isis, guardian of love
and destiny, who has been worshipped for more than
5,000 years! Signs of an ancient rose cult have also been
found in India and in Syria — even the name Syria
comes from the word 'suri', meaning 'land of roses'.
The 'Holy Rose' still grows in Egypt today, and can also
be found in remote areas of Northern Ethiopia (the
former Abyssinia). In 1920, a monk reported finding a
rose growing in an Ethiopian mountain village at an
altitude of 8,000 feet!

Trade in roses also became established at a very early
stage in history. The royal groves of Ur in the
Euphrates–Tigris region have revealed that the
Sumerian King Sargon (2648–2630 BC) returned from

a campaign bringing 'vines, figs and roses'. Caravans wandered from the rivers of Babylonia, taking their cargo with them right across Egypt to North Africa. Arab nomads played a vital role in the distribution of the rose not only throughout the Middle East, but also later by bringing it to Europe.

Botanically speaking, however, it is difficult to locate the exact origin of the first wild rose because the early records are far from complete. What is clear is that from very early times there existed several distinct species of rose which were distributed throughout the northern hemisphere, having two main centres – one in Central Asia and the other in Western Europe. These became known as the 'Old' rose varieties because they formed the basis of all the subsequent hybrids, or 'New' roses.

The historical division between 'Old' and 'New' roses is generally taken to be the year 1800, due to the influence of France's Empress Josephine. From 1808 and 1814 the Empress, wife of Napoleon Bonaparte, established a rose garden at Malmaison (outside Paris) which was unsurpassed. She obtained all the known roses of the time, including the newly arrived Asiatic and Chinese varieties. Their cultivation and propagation became an inspiration to rose-growers throughout the world, and formed the basis for the subsequent hybridization of the innumerable rose varieties.

Since then, roses have been bred as carefully as race-horses, and many new varieties have been developed. Today there are numerous books available on the cultivation of garden roses containing hundreds of lavish, glossy plates illustrating the diversity, beauty and allure of the modern (and often scentless) 'New' rose.

In recent years, however, there has a been a nostalgic return to the appeal of the 'Old' scented rose varieties. Their fragrance, which had often suffered in the pursuit of the perfect form, has also begun to be re-evaluated. The most significant of these original and highly scented 'Old' roses, particularly regarding their subsequent cultivation and (highly successful) hybridization for the production of essential oils, are the following:

Rosa gallica (*R. rubra*) – the 'Gallic Rose'
Rosa damascena – the 'Damask Rose'
Rosa centifolia – the 'Cabbage Rose'

The Gallic Rose
The natural habitat of the Gallic Rose is thought to have been Iran (formerly Persia) and the land between the Black and the Caspian Seas – though its real roots are lost in antiquity. Like the 'Holy Rose', the Gallic Rose originally blossomed in its natural wild state as a simple flower with five petals – mostly of a deep pink or 'rosy'-red colour. Later, how-ever, *R. gallica* also came to exist in a whole range of different forms or subspecies, the best known being *R. gallica* var. *officinalis* – the 'Apothecary Rose' or the 'Red Rose', a shrub of 90 cm to 1.5 m (3 to 5 ft) high with very fragrant, semi-double deep crimson flowers and yellow anthers

(centre). In early times, the petals of this variety were often made into a fragrant powder valued for its pharmaceutical properties. After the Middle Ages it also became known as the 'French Rose' or the 'Rose of Provins' because it was grown in high quantities in the French region of Provence, mainly for use in perfumery. Varieties of the Gallic Rose are still used for the production of essential oils, for example by the British pioneer microbiologist, Peter Wilde.

The Damask Rose

The Damask Rose (*Rosa damascena*) – so called because it was presumed to have been brought originally from Damascus in Syria – bears pink or red, very fragrant double flowers with up to 36 petals each, borne on arching stems reaching to 2 m (7 ft) long. This was the rose most used by the early Arab perfume makers, who introduced it to Europe. It is still used to produce a very high quality essential oil, 'attar of rose' (and absolute), mainly for use in perfumery. Today it is cultivated on a large scale in Bulgaria and Turkey, and to a lesser extent in Russia, India and Iran. It too has been recorded in many different forms or sub-species, notably the 30-petalled variety, 'Trigintipetala'.

The Cabbage Rose

The Cabbage Rose or 'Hundred-leaved Rose' is not, strictly speaking, an 'Old' rose despite its long history, being a complex hybrid between the Gallic Rose, the Damask Rose, the wild 'Dog Rose', and the 'Musk

Rose' (*see below*). Its origins are obscure, though it has been found growing wild in the forests of the Caucasus, where double-flowered specimens are common. It has been called the 'Painter's Rose' because it appears in the artwork of so many of the Old Masters. It is a handsome, bushy shrub, generally 90 cm to 1.5 m (3 to 5 ft) high, bearing large blooms with up to 100 petals each, which can be white through to dark red. It produces a rich, sweet-scented oil or absolute for which it is widely cultivated in Turkey and North Africa (Morocco and Tunis). For centuries a type of Cabbage Rose has been grown in the region of Grasse in France and known as the 'Rose de Mai' – a hybrid between *R. centifolia* and *R. gallica*. This variety can grow to a height of 2 m (7 ft) and has pink to rose-purple flowers. The Cabbage Rose has subsequently given rise to innumerable subspecies, including the 'Moss Rose'.

Other ancient varieties which are still used for the production of essential oils, but on a smaller scale, include the 'Dog Rose' (*Rosa canina*), 'Sweet Briar' (*R. rubiginosa*), the 'Musk Rose' (*R. moscatta*), the 'Tea Rose' (*R. indica*), the 'White Rose' (*Rosa x alba*), and the 'Japanese (or Chinese) Rose' (*R. rugosa*).

Note: See Appendix A for a more detailed description of these rose species.

PART 1

A Medical and
Historical Background

Legend, Myth and Symbolism

Red rose, proud rose, and rose of all my days
Come near me while I sing thy ancient ways...

W. B. Yeats 'The Rose upon the Rood of Time'

For thousands of years the rose has been prized by all cultures alike – indeed, throughout the ages no flower has enjoyed such favour! Classical texts from both East and West contain numerous references to the rose, and a whole range of myths has sprung up and flourished regarding its origins and symbolism. The symbolism of the rose is perhaps one of the richest and most complex associated with any plant, with a universal appeal that transcends time and cultures. As a powerful image of the heart or soul of humanity, the rose has always represented 'love', 'beauty' and 'divinity' along with many other attributes.

'By thy scent my soul is ravished...' wrote the poet Sadi. He, like many other great Persian writers, saw the rose not only as an object of great physical beauty but also as a symbol of spiritual attainment and transcendent desire. In the *Avesta*, the sacred book of Persia which forms the basis of one of the world's oldest religions, the rose is honoured as 'a messenger of the garden of souls'. Rumi (the great thirteenth-century Sufi mystic and poet) called the rose a 'wise loveliness', and a manifestation of the experience of the eternal 'Beloved':

> *Like a rose, I smile with all my body, not only with my*
> *mouth,*
> *For I am — without myself — alone with the King of the*
> *World*

Rumi, Divan-e-Kabir

Among the Sufis, the experience of the sacred was intimately associated with the form and scent of the rose, and the Persian alchemist and mystic Avicenna dedicated a whole book to the virtues of his favoured plant. According to one Persian legend, the nightingale fell in love with the white rose and flew down to embrace it. But she pierced her breast upon its sharp thorns, and from the drops of blood falling on the earth there grew the first deep crimson rose:

> *...And above all, the repeated splendours of glowing*
> *dawns, the profusion of rose gardens, white roses and red*
> *roses, the shades of the rose bushes, the divine presence*
> *flashing in the brilliance of a red rose.*[1]

Ancient Persia is thought to be the birthplace of the cultivated rose, and the first place where roses were planted in beautifully laid out gardens. When the Moslem Arabs conquered Persia in the sixth century, they were so enamoured with the cultivated roses which they found growing there that Islam adopted the rose as central to its own tradition. Indeed, according to Arabic legend, when the prophet Muhammad was taken to heaven a drop of his sweat fell to earth and this became the first rose! In another story, roses come not from the prophet but from the perspiration of a lady, Joun, whose skin is white at dawn but rosy at midday. Later, as the Moslem religion spread to large areas of the known world, the love of the rose went too.

As early as 900 BC, Homer described in the *Iliad* that the shield of Achilles was decorated with roses – as were the shields of the ancient Persian warriors. In addition, the custom which is still known today of strewing roses on the graves of the dead can be traced back to this period. In ancient Greece the rose was held sacred to Aphrodite, goddess of love and beauty. According to Greek legend, the first rose grew out of the white foam that covered Aphrodite at her birth. For the Greeks, the red rose is said to have issued from the blood of her beloved Adonis after he was attacked by a wild boar – the word 'rosa' derives from the Greek word 'rodon', meaning red:

...the crown jewel of the flowers, and the royal purple of wise men, the mirror of beauty. Full of love she is Aphrodite's servant; with fragrant leaves shining brightly she sways above the foliage bathing in the smiles of Zephyr.

Achilles Tatios, 139 BC

As the cult of the rose spread over the whole of ancient Greece and beyond, so did the mythology surrounding it. One of the oldest Roman stories is of Flora, who upon finding the corpse of a beautiful nymph, a daughter of the Dryads, transformed her body into the first rose with the assistance of Venus and the Graces. Apollo then blessed the flower, Bacchus supplied the nectar, Vertumnus the perfume, while Pomona gave her fruit and Flora crowned her with beauty. According to another legend, the first rose was said to have originally been white in colour, the red varieties coming into being when a thorn pierced the foot of Venus – her blood staining the petals crimson.

Although the rose had been revered by many early civilizations, with the Romans worship of the rose took on unsurpassed proportions. Indeed, no other culture has been as obsessed with the rose in a literal sense, as that of ancient Rome ... they even created a holiday, 'Rosalia', to consummate their passion for the flower!

Roses were strewn at public ceremonies and banquets; rose-water bubbled through the emperor's fountains and the public baths surged with it; in the public amphitheaters, crowds sat under sun awnings steeped in rose perfume; rose petals were used as pillow stuffings; people wore garlands of roses in their hair; they ate rose pudding; their medicines, love potions, and aphrodisiacs all contained roses. No Bacchanalia, the Romans' official orgy, was complete without an excess of roses... At one banquet, Nero ... spent the equivalent of fifty thousand pounds just on roses – and one of his guests smothered to death under a shower of rose petals.[2]

In 220 AD, Athenaeus mentions that rose petals were strewn eight inches deep upon the ground in Cleopatra's private chambers when she first met Mark Antony! In the early years of the Roman Empire, the rose was linked with Venus, the Goddess of love – but in latter years, as the Empire declined and decayed, it came to stand for vice and immoral behaviour. After the fall of the Empire, the Roman Catholic Church thus condemned the rose as a heathen flower. The Church was particularly contemptuous of the old pagan custom of offering wreaths of roses to the dead:

If they are blessed, they do not need them – and if they are lost, they won't have any pleasure in them![3]

But the rose was not an image that could be wiped clean from human consciousness. The custom of offering roses to the dead persisted, and since the symbolism of the rose could not be eradicated, it gradually became incorporated into early Christian mythology. The red rose became the symbol of Jesus' blood – the five petals representing the five wounds of Christ – and a sign of martyrs and saints. The custom of decorating churches with roses and carving roses over the entrance to the confessional as an emblem of discretion also dates from Roman times. In the Roman story, the rose was given by Cupid as a bribe to Harpocrates, the god of Silence. Henceforth, a rose was suspended above Roman banqueting tables to indicate that anything said beneath it was to be held in strictest confidence – the origin of the expression 'sub-rosa'.

To the early Christian mystics, the rose (especially the white rose) was also associated with the Virgin Mary and the ideal of 'purity' or 'divine love'. The Madonna is often depicted in a garden of roses in icon paintings. Here, the rose indicates Mary's love for the child Jesus, while more profoundly it suggests the love required for the nurturing of the Christ principle within. According to tradition, the Virgin appeared to St Dominic bearing a chaplet of roses, and the first rosary was made in commemoration of this vision. Rosaries originally consisted of 165 dried, carefully rolled up rose petals, sometimes darkened with lampblack as a preservative. One of the oldest Maria hymns says:

> *Fresh rose, pure rose, chaste rose,*
> *Without thorns, rose flowering,*
> *Fruits bearing, burning red,*
> *More than a rose, whiter than a lily.*[4]

During the following centuries, roses became more and more widespread as the Crusaders returned to Europe bringing with them new and old varieties. In the days of chivalry, a chaplet of roses was granted to gallant knights for acts of bravery, and the image of the rose became associated with sovereignty. Different types of roses were increasingly used in royal heraldry, as in Britain's 'Wars of the Roses', the thirteenth-century feud between the House of York (the white rose) and the House of Lancaster (the red rose). The Tudor rose of Elizabeth I bore the motto *Rosa sine spina* ('a rose without a thorn'), and the wild dog rose (*Rosa canina*) remains the royal flower of England. The British King or Queen is still anointed at the coronation ceremony with a 'holy oil' containing rose essence, the recipe for which dates back to the twelfth century.

During the Middle Ages, the rose naturally became the favoured flower of the famous 'troubadours' and often featured in their love poetry:

Maiden may I go with thee to thy rose garden?
I would lead thee, sweet love, to the place where the red
   roses grow.[5]

In Elizabethan times the rose was also used as an image of the transient nature of love, as in the well-known verse by Herrick:

   'Gather ye rosebuds while ye may...'

It was fashionable at this time to use a posy of flowers to convey messages of the heart: a red rose meant passion; a white rose, purity or innocence; a yellow rose stood for jealousy or falsehood! A single red rose is still offered today as a token of love. It is remarkable that over thousands of years, the rose's symbolic meaning has remained virtually intact, representing the most profound and far-reaching ideals of human aspiration:

   The single rose is, in essence, a symbol of completion, of
   consummate achievement and perfection.[6]

CHAPTER TWO

The Traditional Medicinal Uses of the Rose

The rose distils a healing balm,
the beating pulse of pain to calm.

Anacreon

Roses have been used medicinally since the earliest times. In ancient Persia, the birthplace of the rose, rosewater was regarded as something of a panacea, while oils and fats saturated with rose petals were used in religious ceremonies and for balms of all kinds. A paste of pounded rose petals mixed with honey was taken as a remedy for angina and tuberculosis, while an infusion of dried flowers was used as a tea to alleviate diarrhoea and (by women) leucorrhoea.

Preparations made from roses also feature strongly in traditional Chinese, Indian, Egyptian and Arabian medicine. In China, the flowers of a highly scented variety, *Rosa rugosa* ('mei gui hua') are still used in the form of a decoction as a blood tonic and to help stimulate stagnant liver energy, or 'qi' (the Chinese word for energy). The petals are also used for digestive or menstrual irregularities, especially to help relieve heavy periods. A rose extract and rose oil made from *Rosa rugosa* are also used in China, as Li Shih-Chen describes:

> *Its nature is cooling, its taste is sweet with a slight bitterishness, and it acts especially on the spleen and liver, promoting the circulation of the blood. It is prescribed in the form of an extract for haematemesis, and the flowers are used in all diseases of the liver, to scatter abscesses, and in blood diseases generally... Essence of Rose is made by distilling the flowers of* Rosa rugosa. *Its medicinal action is upon the liver, stomach, and blood. It drives away melancholy.*[1]

In India, likewise, the rose has a long history of traditional usage. In Ayurvedic medicine, *Rosa damascena* is thought to have a regulating and revitalizing effect, being particularly beneficial for the heart, eyes and the skin:

> *It is a laxative, and a tonic; and increases semen, and enhances the beauty of the complexion. It has a combined bitter and sweet taste. It is a digestive, restores the balance of 'tridoshas' (primary qualities) and it is highly efficacious in blood impurities.*[2]

In ancient Egypt, a rose unguent was prepared by infusing the flowers in fat for use in the treatment of various skin complaints and as an ingredient in cosmetics and perfumes. Rose oil together with vinegar and chicory juice was considered an effective cure for headaches. However, it was the early Arab physicians who were the first to perfect the distillation of rose oil as we know it today. They employed the oil to combat an almost endless list of complaints, including:

> ...headache, sun and heat stroke, hangover, migraine, stomatitis, loss of appetite, gastritis, gastric ulcer, constipation, ulcerous colitis, haemorrhoids, fissures, hepatic diseases, eye affections, dental caries, opium intoxication, insect and snake bites, wounds that did not heal properly, itching and burns.[3]

At one time, the rose also held a prominent place in the Western medical tradition. As early as the fourth century BC, Hippocrates (the 'Father of Medicine'), described how a perfumed 'rose oil' was prepared in Anatolia by macerating fresh roses in olive oil. In addition, he prescribed rose medicaments specifically for gynaecological and obstetric conditions. Then, in the first century AD, Dioscorides compiled the first extensive *Materia Medica* by drawing on traditional Greek and Egyptian herbal lore ... a work which was regarded as an authoritative guide well into the seventeenth century. In this volume, the rose is recommended as a remedy for a wide variety of complaints, including headache, eye and ear disorders, and gastro-intestinal illnesses.

In his *Natural History*, Pliny the Elder (a Roman contemporary of Dioscorides writing in AD 76) claimed that the rose (*R. gallica*), prepared in various ways, could be used in the treatment of 32 conditions. These included inflammation of the eyes, the ears and the mouth, stomach ache, toothache, insomnia, the healing of wounds, and for what he called 'purification of the mind'. Pliny also described how the wealthy Romans filled their baths with rose petals to keep the body young and alluring – a method also employed as a cure for hangover! In a preparation known as *diapasmata*, or 'powdered perfume', petals were dried and finely ground then sprinkled on the body to inhibit perspiration.

Throughout Europe during the Middle Ages, the Gallic Rose was the principal variety grown in monastery gardens; the dried petals were commonly available from the apothecary – thus the name 'Apothecary Rose'. The dried flowers were mainly used as herb to be strewn on the ground in place of carpets, for pot pourris, or as a herbal 'simple'.

Roses were in fact prepared in a vast and ingenious variety of ways: an ointment of roses was used to soothe headaches; a syrup to 'comfort the heart'; rose leaves mixed with mint were applied as a poultice to 'quiet the over-heated spirits'; infusions of rose leaves and petals, or the petals ingested in honey, were employed as a remedy for coughs, while a rose conserve was prescribed for liver complaints. Rose vinegar was recommended for several disorders including nose bleeds, indigestion, headaches and hangovers, while rosewater was used to soothe sore eyes. At one time, the roots of the wild Dog Rose (*R. canina*) were even used to treat those afflicted by rabies – 'the bites of mad dogs'. Rose oil also had its uses:

> In the Middle Ages, physicians such as Walafried Stabon of Reichenau, Odo of Maine and Arnold of Villanova used rose oil for complaints ranging from infected wounds to diarrhoea. It was also used in various applications as a treatment for heart diseases, having a cardionic effect and reducing heart trembling.[4]

Nicholas Culpeper, the well-known British herbalist and astrologer writing in the early seventeenth century, dedicated more space to the rose than to any other herb:

> Red roses strengthen the heart, the stomach, the liver, and the retentive faculty; they mitigate the pains that arise from heat, cool inflammations, procure rest and sleep, stay both the whites and reds in women ... red rosewater is cooling, cordial, refreshing, quickening the weak and

faint spirits, used either in meats or broths or to wash the
temples, to smell at the nose, or to smell the sweet vapours
out of a perfume pot, or cast into a hot fire-shovel. It is of
much use against the redness and inflammations of the
eyes to bathe therewith and the temples of the head ... oil
of roses is used to cool hot inflammation or swellings ...
also put into ointments and plasters that are cooling and
binding... [5]

The Damask Rose, according to Culpeper, was in
addition a 'cephalic', being uplifting to the mind on
account of its fragrance. Gerarde, an early European
herbalist (1545–1612) tells us that rosewater
'bringeth sleep which also the fresh roses themselves
provoke through their sweet and pleasant smell'.
Robert Lovell, writing later in the seventeenth century, also devoted several pages to the rose, and he
too made particular note of the effect of its scent:

Oleum rosarum (the oil of roses) is a good perfume; a drop
or two cheres the heart, brain, animal and vitall spirits. [6]

It is clear that all the old herbalists were in agree-
ment that roses were very valuable medicinal agents
– the Gallic Rose especially being highly esteemed
for its cooling, astringent, tonic, regulating and revitalizing effects. However, the eighteenth century saw
a decline in traditional remedies as belief in a scientific approach to medicine took hold of the public
imagination. Chemical drugs replaced the naturally

derived herbal 'simples' and the medical pharma-copoeias became increasingly filled with synthetical-ly-derived substitutes. Over the following centuries the therapeutic value of the rose was consequently gradually eroded in favour of its perfumery use and purely decorative appeal. It is only in the twentieth century that the traditional therapeutic values of the rose have been reassessed!

The Rose as a Twentieth-Century Remedy

A rose is a rose is a rose...

Gertrude Stein, from 'I am a Rose' in *Sacred Emily*

Despite its rich traditional heritage as a folk remedy, by the beginning of the twentieth century the rose had almost vanished from Western medicine. In 1907, the rose growers of the Provence region in France obtained a government warrent that their unguents derived from roses would be used in all French public and military hospitals. In Britain, however, only the wild or common Dog Rose (*R. canina*) retained its medicinal uses. During the Second World War, for example, it was common for children to be dosed with rose hip syrup, due to its high vitamin C content. The chopped fruits are also still occasionally used as a folk remedy in the form of a decoction for a variety of disorders:

...two and a half teaspoons finely cut fruit per cup of water, boiled for 10 minutes to achieve optimum vitamin C content, several times a day against constipation, colds, gall disorders, and disorders of the kidneys, and bladder; also as a spring tonic and against general exhaustion.[1]

Red rose petals from *R. gallica* were listed in the *British Herbal Pharmacopoeia* until the 1930s, mainly as a mild astringent and to flavour other medicines. By 1983, however, only the hips of *R. canina* are mentioned in connection with gastritis, diarrhoea and poldipsia, and as 'a dietary supplement as a natural source of vitamin C, together with small amounts of A and B vitamins'.[2] What happened to all the ancient uses of the rose ... were they just 'old wives' tales', or do they in fact have a sound scientific basis?

Over the last 20 years, several Bulgarian scientists have been researching the possible medical applications of the rose, and numerous papers have been published specifically on rose oil. The results have shown that in many cases rose oil lives up to the ancient traditional benefits ascribed to it. For example, it was demonstrated that rose oil can:

- reduce high blood-pressure and arrhythmia of the heart
- counteract the effects of isoprenaline (an old anti-asthma drug), which stimulates the heart to beat more strongly

- protect against gastrointestinal ulceration
- have an antispasmodic effect (easing spasms and convulsions)
- protect against bronchial asthma (as tested on guinea pigs)
- have a powerful antibacterial action.[3]

A rose ointment (Rosalin) was also tested against numerous micro-organisms with outstanding results. Apart from having a generally soothing and analgesic effect, this ointment was found to be especially beneficial in treating the following cases:

- acute radiodermatitis – dermatitis (dry skin or burns) caused by radiotherapy
- late radionecrosis – necrosis (cell death) caused by radiotherapy
- cancer patients who had received radiation therapy
- ulcers (gave good results in a total of 154 cases where antibiotics had been ineffective).

In addition, a rose oil medicament (Rosanol), taken in the form of capsules containing 33 mg of pure rose oil, was shown to be effective for many disturbances of the bile-forming function of the liver. In a clinical study carried out in the former Soviet Union, rose oil was found to increase the secretion of bile fluid in rats; the study suggested that rose oil may also stimulate hepatic (liver) bile formation in humans, especially the synthesis of bile acids, thus making it valuable in the treatment of several liver and gall bladder complaints.

In another study, rosewater was found to have almost identical properties to that of rose oil and, taken as a drink (diluted in mineral water), demonstrated excellent therapeutic properties, especially in cases of gastro-intestinal, renal and liver diseases. Rosewater was also highly recommended in this study as a cosmetic ingredient due to its softening, hydrating, stimulating, astringent and disinfectant properties.

Professor Dietrich Wabner (Head of the Applied Electrochemistry and Environmental Research Group at the Technical University of Munich) has also been researching the properties of rose oil and rose products over a number of years, and looking anew at its possible medicinal and cosmetic applications. He has focused particularly on the possible applications of rose oil in the treatment of headaches, migraine, skin care, the common cold and as a remedy for the herpes simplex virus, which causes cold sores. In his article 'Rose Oil: Its Use In Therapy and Cosmetics' he compares the ancient uses of rose oil with the results of several modern studies:

> *Modern scientific research was able to confirm some of the medicinal properties of roses as applied by the ancient*

Indians and Chinese and later by Culpeper and his con-
temporaries ... I tried some of the formulations found in
the literature myself, and I can confirm many of the effects
of rose oil ... I believe that rose oil has enormous thera-
peutic potential.[4]

In his work he confined himself to the Bulgarian and
Turkish oils (*Rosa damascena*) and found that, besides
having a powerful effect on the skin, they also
demonstrated a profound emotional effect. He discovered that the Turkish/Moroccan rose oil has a
more narcotic effect than the Bulgarian type – and
has been shown to be a more potent aphrodisiac! He
could not confirm, however, the classification of rose
oil as exclusively 'female' or 'yin' in character, as
tradition might suggest:

The harmonizing effect of rose oil makes it clear that no
definite yin character is at work. Rose oil shows a balance
of yin and yang – relaxation and stimulation are both
possible. The same is true of the aphrodisiac effect. It is
not strongly sexual but creates an erotic atmosphere.[5]

This corresponds with the research of the French
doctor Gattefossé, who mentions that, according to
Dr Marceval, rose essence stimulates the sexual centres and acts as an aphrodisiac. Dr Gattefossé also
cites Gregoire's work on frog hearts, in which the
latter demonstrated that rose, like 'neroli essence

and orangeflower water are tranquillizers which slow the heart beat substantially'.[6]

This tends to suggest that, while rose essence can indeed stimulate the brain and uplift the spirits, at the same time it reduces the heart rate and blood-pressure and soothes the nerves. Research into the effects of different odours on mood has also shown that stimulation and relaxation are not mutually exclusive states. In this context, rose could be said to be an 'adaptogen' – in other words, it can increase both stimulation and relaxation. In her pioneering book, *The Secret of Life and Youth*, Madame Maury also regards rose oil as primarily regulating in its effect:

> As a well-known aphrodisiac, it is used in the Hindu pharmocopoeia reinforced with sandalwood. Our own experiences have taught us that the rose has a considerable influence on the female sexual organs. Not by stimulus, but on the contrary, by cleansing and regulating their functions.[7]

Madame Maury also recommended rose for all types of cosmetic preparations, especially for ageing skin, as well as prescribing it as a means of regulating the appetite and overcoming anorexia. She also has this to say about the essence of rose:

> But the rose procures us one thing above all: a feeling of well being, even of happiness, and the individual under its influence will develop an amiable tolerance.[8]

In modern aromatherapy practice, rose essence is used as a mild anti-depressant and is employed especially for emotional shock, bereavement, grief and the treatment of melancholy. According to writer and aromatherapist Patricia Davis, it is especially valuable for women who lack confidence in their own sexuality or who suffer from frigidity.

> *Due to its soothing action on the nerves, rose essence is recommended for headaches, migraine, PMT and other stress-related disorders. According to recent research, its comforting, warm and uplifting fragrance can also help to focus the mind.*[9]

Modern research and the current therapeutic applications of rose oil increasingly confirm ancient traditional lore. Thus, the Arabian doctor Avicenna was no doubt correct when he wrote in the tenth century AD:

> *Rose oil increases the might of the brain and quickness of the mind.*

Cultivation, Production and Quality Control

Rose oil is ... inimitable, peerless and an absolute necessity.[1]

It is difficult to be sure exactly when and where rose oil was first prepared. Sanskrit literature describes the method employed in ancient India for making a 'rose unguent' or 'oil of rose' by maceration. It is possible that the ancient Egyptians prepared an early form of 'oleum rosarum' by heating a vessel containing the rose petals dissolved in water over a fire, then collecting the oil in thick wool suspended above the vessel as the distillate evaporated. It is more likely, however, that like that of the early Greeks and Romans, Egyptian 'rose oil' was really a type of ointment or pomade made by infusing the fragrant petals in olive oil (sesame oil was recommended by Theophrastus) or a fatty base, rather than what we would now call a true 'attar' or 'otto' of rose.

It is clear that the production of rosewater preceded that of rose oil, for as early as 810 BC records show that the province of Faristan in Persia was obliged to deliver some 30,000 vessels of rosewater to Baghdad.[2] Faristan and the area around Shiraz appear to have been the principal centres for its production at this time, for these regions also sent considerable quantities to India, China, Yemen and Egypt.

Persia is also generally credited as being the birthplace of the cultivated rose, and legend has it that the discovery of 'attar' was conceived amid their famous rose gardens. For the wedding of the Princess Nour-Djihan to the Emperor Djihanguyr, the fountains and canal encircling the royal gardens were filled with rosewater. Later, while walking in the gardens with her husband, the princess noticed that a rich honey-scented residue had formed on top of the water, due to the heat of the sun. It was skimmed off and collected – and this, so the story goes, was the origin of the first 'attar' of rose. In fact, the term 'attar' or 'a'thara' is simply an old Arabic word meaning 'scent' or 'perfume'; in the Middle East, rose 'otto' or 'attar' is still referred to as 'athar gul' or 'aettr gyl'.

In the tenth century AD the Arab physician, Avicenna, perfected the art of distillation using the refrigerated coil method. By employing (most probably) the double damask rose in his experiments, he produced the first high-quality rose oil, or rose attar.

The type of rose grown in Iran (Persia) and Saudi Arabia today is the 30-petalled 'Rose of Damascus', or *Rosa damascena* 'Trigintipetala'. This species is also the mainstay of rose oil production internationally. The merit of this variety is that it is easy to cultivate and can produce a high quality 'attar' simply by distillation. In Arabic culture, an oil produced by distillation is preferred, since the presence of alcohol (as in the case of solvent extraction – *see below*) is unacceptable to those of Islamic faith. The major disadvantage of *R. damascena* is that it flowers only once per season and the harvest lasts a mere 40 days!

During the harvest, the rose petals are handpicked before dawn: the oil content is highest during the morning and can decrease by as much as 30 per cent if left until later in the day. Quality and yield are very much affected by the weather and storage conditions. Humidity in particular can damage the petals, thus distillation generally takes place within hours of picking. The type of distillation equipment in use today was originally developed at the end of the nineteenth century, although the simple copper field stills first used have been replaced by large-scale, stainless steel industrial units.

Most modern processors still use the traditional steam distillation technique, mixing about half a tonne of freshly picked flower heads with one-and-a-half tonnes of water in a still. Over two tonnes of rose petals are required to produce 1 kg (2.2 lb) of essential oil, which is why it remains a costly and highly valued commodity. The petals are then hydro-distilled and the oil and water collected. The top layer of the distillate is separated by decantation, the remaining liquid (rosewater) is then redistilled separately. Strictly speaking, rose attar is not simply a distilled oil but a blend of decanted and recovered oils.

'Trigintipetala' is also the variety cultivated in the famous 'Rose Valley', on the southern slopes of the Balkans, in central Bulgaria. Throughout Bulgaria's turbulent history, from the Ottoman Empire through Russian domination to recent independence, this rose has triumphed. Today, the fragrance of Bulgarian rose 'attar' is still considered to be the highest quality available, and is in great demand for exclusive perfumery products.

In Turkey there are at least 200 industrial stills dedicated to the production of rose oil. One of the largest Turkish distillers, Gulbirlik, is a farmers' co-operative established about 80 years ago with the financial support of the government. Each year, like the Iranian Golab Company, it sends 500 litres of rosewater to Mecca, to wash the holy walls each day. There are now five major distillers in Turkey, between them producing around 3,500 kg of rose attar annually.

Apart from Bulgaria, the Arab states, and Turkey, other countries including Russia, China and India also produce rose oil, though in smaller quantities. A small amount of 'attar' or 'otto' has also been produced in France for at least 150 years, using a variety of the Hundred-petalled Rose or *Rosa centifolia*, 'Rose de Mai'. This species, however, does not perform as well as *R. damascena* upon distillation, and is therefore mainly employed for the production of a rose concrete and absolute (*see below*). A rose leaf absolute is also produced for selective use in France.

The major source of rose absolute today is Morocco, using *Rosa centifolia*. The process generally used to produce absolutes and concretes is that of solvent extraction, or 'dry cleaning'. Hexane (a petroleum hydrocarbon) is the most widely used, but acetone, benzene and methylene chloride are also sometimes employed. In hexane extraction the flowers are stirred up in the solvent, which absorbs the vital ingredients. The hexane is then evaporated off by boiling the solution at 60°C. The resulting concrete is treated with alcohol, which dissolves the essential oils but not the waxes and other components. The alcohol is then distilled away by boiling at 78°C. The resulting product is a viscous reddish-orange liquid with a sweet, spicy-floral tenacious fragrance. It is highly valued in perfumery work for 'rounding off' floral compositions.

In recent years, the British microbiologist and engineer Dr Peter Wilde has developed an innovative extraction technique for the production of a new type of rose absolute in the UK. By using a non-toxic solvent which is only liquid at minus 30°C, all the vital ingredients of the rose fragrance are captured without the loss of any of the 'top notes' which inevitably disperse at higher temperatures. Dr Wilde employs a variety of 'old-fashioned' roses in his production, including R. *damascena* 'Triginpetala', and also a Gallic Rose 'Belle de Cresy' and two Bourbon roses, 'Madame Isaac Pereire' and 'Louise Odier'. His sophisticated low-temperature apparatus has been very costly to set up, and this has made the oil expensive. Cost has also been one of the main obstacles in another newly developed technique: the liquid 'Super Critical' CO_2 process. In both cases, however, the resulting absolute has remarkable depth and richness. It is also entirely free of any undesirable residue, which is usually the case in aromatic absolutes produced by solvent extraction, although the actual quantities of residue are generally minute.

The quality and composition of a rose oil (or absolute) can thus vary greatly according to where the roses are grown, cultivation methods, exact botanical origin and the type of extraction process used. Moreover, the demand for rose oil in the perfumery industry has led to generations of chemists trying to isolate the individual constituents and to create a good synthetic imitation or 'nature identical' product. This has proved impossible for a number of reasons, not least because of the complexity of the formulation. Rose oil and rose absolute contain at least 400 different constituents, some of which do not even have a name! Many of these are present in minute quantities, yet still play important roles in the overall odour and effectiveness of the rose oil (or absolute) produced.

Nevertheless, most modern perfumes on the market today contain synthetic rose substitutes, and the majority of commercial rosewaters are 'reconstructed' or 'reconstituted'. Rose oil is itself also widely subject to adulteration using a whole range of additives. This may include blending it with other oils (such as palmarosa or guaic wood oil) or 'extending' the oil with constituents such as 'geraniol' or an artificially produced chemical such as phenyl ethyl alcohol. Since adulterated or 'nature identical' oils cannot be substituted for the genuine oil for therapeutic use, modern trace analysis (gas chromatography) is a valuable method for checking the composition of an oil. Using gas chromatography, a skilled technician can detect impurities by reading the precise position of each peak on the graph which indicates the amount of each constituent present. A trained 'nose is still however, a very good guide to guality.'

Note: Rose oil and rose absolute are commonly called 'rose oil', strictly speaking this is inaccurate.

See Appendix B for a detailed account of the chemical constituents of rose oil.

A Summary of the Properties and Applications of Rose Oil

There is an old saying that roses are good for 'the skin and the soul' — and perhaps there is a great deal of truth in this! The rose's rich, floral scent together with its valuable medicinal properties means that it lends itself particularly well to all types of cosmetic, perfumery and toiletry products.

But where rose oil comes into its own, as it were, is in the field of psychosomatic conditions, where physical and the emotional factors are interrelated. In the words of Professor Dietrich Wabner, who has spent several years researching the properties of rose oil:

> I can say that for me rose oil is a remedy for both skin and soul. It has a strong harmonizing effect, and in this way works against all kind of stress.[1]

In mythology, too, the rose has always been associated with the soul or heart — with love, sexuality and women. It therefore should come as no surprise that the rose is a traditional remedy for problems involving menstruation, PMT, and menopausal and sexual difficulties of both physical and emotional origin:

Therefore, although traditionally rose oil has a wide range of applications, the main areas it can benefit may be summarized as follows:

- skin care and perfumery
- stress-related conditions
- reproduction and sexuality.

SKIN CARE AND PERFUMERY

Rose oil's excellent **antiseptic**, **bactericidal** and **anti-inflammatory** properties make it a very valuable remedy for all types of inflamed, irritated and infected skin conditions, such as minor cuts, cold sores, eczema and all kinds of rashes, especially those of an allergic nature. As a mild (local) **anaesthetic**, it helps soothe pain and, since it has a pronounced **cicatrizant** (wound-healing) or **regenerative** effect on cell tissue, it is especially beneficial for dry, sensitive or ageing skin, having an overall **rejuvenating** effect.

Rose oil and rosewater are in addition good **softening**, **astringent** and **deodorizing** agents, and as such make valuable ingredients for facial and body

lotions. Although rose oil is an exquisite perfume in
its own right, it is also used to 'round off' a blend of
fragrances, and is found as a component in over 46
per cent of men's and 98 per cent of women's perfumes. These factors, together with its **low toxicity** and excellent **compatibility with all skin
types**, make rose an ideal component for most cosmetics.

STRESS-RELATED CONDITIONS

Rose oil is valuable for relieving stress, for a number
of reasons:

• First, it has a **regulating** action on the heart and
  vascular system by reducing high blood-pressure
  and normalizing arrhythmia or palpitations, while
  at the same time acting as a general tonic for the
  heart and capillaries.
• Secondly, it has a pronounced **antispasmodic**
  effect, valuable for alleviating all types of muscu-
  lar contraction brought on by stress. It helps
  soothes indigestion, yet as a **stomachatic** it
  improves the appetite and strengthens the whole
  digestive system. In addition, it increases bile
  production and acts as a mild **laxative** and
  depurative (purifying) agent, which is beneficial
  in cases of gastro-intestinal, renal and liver com-

plaints, especially stomach ulcers, gall stones and congestion of the liver.

Note: These latter properties are, however, more pronounced when rose is taken internally as a tea or tincture.

- Thirdly, it has a soothing effect on the nervous system and, as a mild **sedative**, can help to induce relaxation and sleep.

The triple action of rose on the vascular, digestive and nervous systems, and more particularly the nature of its action, render it particularly suitable for the conditions of stress which are becoming more and more common today: nervous tension, peptic ulcers, heart disease, and so on.[2]

But of equal, or even greater significance in this context is the effect that rose exerts psychologically. Its fragrance has long been regarded as **cephalic** – that is, it has an uplifting and clarifying effect on the mind. This also helps account for its **anti-depressant** qualities, and why it is recommended in aromatherapy for emotional upsets, especially those involving the heart, such as grief, postnatal depression, feelings of loss, bereavement, jealousy and relationship problems.

REPRODUCTION AND SEXUALITY

Love is the bridge between sexuality and the soul ...
and it is in the image of the rose, 'the mystic centre',
that sacred and profane love unite. Why, in all cultures alike, is the rose associated with the Goddess of
Love in all her various aspects? Is it the scent, the
beauty of its form, the physical or psychological
properties of the rose ... or is it a combination of all
these factors?

> *Rose is, above all, the flower of love, both human and
> Divine ... In this one flower the archetypes of Madonna
> and Whore are brought together... It brings healing to the
> Heart Chakra and helps it to open again when grief has
> caused it to close down, but where the chakra is already
> open, Rose strengthens its energy enabling love energy to
> radiate out... Rose has an equal affinity with the Sacral
> Chakra, the centre of creativity, sex and conception. It is
> a gentle aphrodisiac and facilitates creativity in all the
> arts, but above all, by uniting within itself the human and
> Divine aspects of love, Rose helps to spiritualize sexual
> relationships.*[3]

The rich sensuality of the rose is particularly appar-
ent in the Turkish and Moroccan rose oil, with its
narcotic scent and **aphrodisiac** effect. This type
of oil is especially helpful for women suffering from
frigidity. Conversely, rose also has the reputation of

increasing the production of semen, and may well be of use in cases of male impotence.

Rose oil also helps to **regulate** the menstrual cycle, is a gentle **emmenagogue** (promoting menstruation), and cleanses the womb of impurities. In general, it acts as a **uterine tonic** and may be used to treat minor disorders of the genito-urinary system such as leucorrhoea, loss of uterine muscle tone, or slight prolapse of the womb. At one time it was even used to treat gonorrhoea!

SECONDARY PROPERTIES

Realistically speaking, pure rose oil is so expensive that it would be impractical to use it for complaints that could just as easily be dealt with in a more economical fashion. For example, although it may be a useful prophylactic agent, with good expectorant and antitussive properties for colds, coughs, bronchitis, sore throats, laryngitis and even tuberculosis, there are many other (less expensive) remedies which will also suffice in this respect, such as tea tree, eucalyptus or sage.

At one time, infusions of the red rose were recommended for diarrhoea, nausea, vomiting and coughing or vomiting blood, because of its binding and astringent properties. On the other hand, the Damask Rose was also used as a gentle purgative, and employed for constipation due its mild cathartic effect. Such applications, however, require internal use, and are largely outdated now in any case. The same is true of its anthelmintic (worm-expelling) and antiparasitic properties, both of which lie beyond the scope of this book.

Methods of Use, Safety Data and Storage Precautions

METHODS OF USE

Pure rose oil (or absolute) is very expensive — although not as expensive as it is often made out to be! Despite its price, natural rose oil makes an exquisite perfume and a valuable remedy, even when used in minute amounts. Because of its rich, concentrated consistency and its powerful, tenacious fragrance, it can be used in lower proportions than many other essential oils — up to a tenth of a per cent less! For these reasons rose oil is usually sold already diluted in a bland base oil such as fractionated coconut oil. It is best to buy an oil where the dilution is clearly stated, rather than a product where the exact dilution is not specified. This can then be used as a perfume directly on the skin, or may be used for making skin creams, bath oils, remedies, etc.

THE INSTRUCTIONS GIVEN IN THIS BOOK ARE
FOR A 5 PER CENT ROSE DILUTION, UNLESS
OTHERWISE STATED.

Bath

Add 15–20 drops of rose oil (5 per cent in dilution)
to the bath water once the bath is full, then relax in
the water for at least 10 minutes.

For bathing the feet or hands, add approximately
12–16 drops of rose oil to a bowl or shallow bath of
warm water and soak for 5–10 minutes.

To make a luxurious bath preparation, buy a quan-
tity of plain bath salts and fill a decorative glass jar to
the top. Add up to 5 ml of rose oil (5 per cent in
dilution) to the jar, shake gently and then keep well
sealed. The salts will turn a pale pinkish colour and,
when added to the bath water, impart a lovely delicate fragrance.

Compress / Poultice

A simple disinfectant compress can be made by dip-
ping a flannel (face cloth) or piece of cotton wool
(cotton ball) in a bowl of water (steaming hot or ice
cold, as required) to which has been added approximately 6–10 drops of rose oil (5 per cent in dilution). A poultice can be made by adding a few drops
of rose to a clay or kaolin base, mixing well and
applying where necessary.

Direct / Neat Application

Rose oil (or absolute) is available in a neat form, although it is much more expensive than the diluted product (*see* Useful Addresses, *page 112*). Pure rose oil is safe to use direct from the bottle as an exclusive perfume – dab with the fingertips or use a cotton bud (cotton swab). It can also be used therapeutically in minute amounts.

Note: Most essential oils should not be used neat on the skin.

Drying Roses and Pot Pourris

Pick the roses on a dry day after any dew has evaporated. Choose those with long stems and firm buds, just as they are beginning to open. Remove all thorns and lower leaves, then tie them together in bunches of 3 to 5. To air-dry the roses, hang them upside down in a dark, dry, cool place where there is plenty of ventilation. Once hung, the roses will continue to open for about three of four days. The drying process takes about two weeks, depending on temperatures.

To make pot pourris, the rose petals can be dried individually on sheets of paper. Then layer 1 litre of rose petals with 250 ml coarse sea salt and leave in a dry place for two weeks, stirring daily. Add 2 tbsp ground orris root powder and ¼ ml of rose oil (5 per cent in dilution). Stir well, then seal in a crock and leave for two months to mature.

Although rose is one of the most classic ingredients, pot pourris can of course include many other fragrant ingredients. For example, a spicy blend can be made by mixing a base of rose petals with bay leaves, cinnamon sticks, cloves or grated nutmeg together with the orris root before storage. Other essential oils can also be added to the blend to enhance the scent or to revitalize it.

Gargling and Dental Care

For the treatment of mouth and gum infections such as mouth ulcers, add 10–20 drops of rose oil (5 per cent in dilution) to a glass of warm water, mix well, then rinse the mouth and/or gargle.

Inhalation

Add up to 16 drops to a tissue or handkerchief for inhalation throughout the day (or to a pillow for night use). For respiratory complaints, make a steam inhalation by adding about 10 drops of rose oil (5 per cent in dilution) to a bowl of steaming water. Cover your head with a towel and breathe deeply for about 5–10 minutes with your eyes closed.

Massage

Before being applied to the skin for massage purposes, rose (like other essential oils) should always be mixed with a light vegetable oil carrier or base such as sweet almond oil, jojoba or grapeseed – although sunflower or soya oil will also suffice. Jojoba oil (being a liquid wax) does not go rancid, nor does fractionated coconut oil – otherwise a little wheat-germ oil should be added to the blend to prolong its shelf life.

For massage purposes, the dilution for most essential oils should generally be in the region of 2–3 per cent. However, since rose oil/absolute is very concentrated, it is still effective when it is used at only one tenth of the concentration of most other oils. Half a millilitre of pure rose oil is equivalent to about 10 drops of pure rose oil or 200 drops of rose (5 per cent dilution)! When using rose oil in a 5 per cent dilution, a useful guide is simply to add the same number of drops as the base oil measured in millilitres – this gives a 0.25 per cent dilution:

- 200 ml base oil
- 200 drops rose oil
  (5 per cent in dilution)

- 100 ml base oil
- 100 drops rose oil
  (5 per cent dilution)

- 50 ml base oil
- 50 drops rose oil
  (5 per cent)

- 1 tbsp *(approx. 15 ml base oil)*
- 15 drops rose oil
  (5 per cent)

- 1 tsp *(approx. 5 ml base oil)*
- 5 drops rose oil
  (5 per cent)

For a 0.5 per cent dilution, add twice as many drops to the base. For a 1 per cent dilution, add 4 times as many drops. Rose oil is also usually blended with other essential oils such as lavender, geranium or chamomile for massage purposes.

Sitz Bath/Douche

For vaginal and genito-urinary infections, add 12–18 drops of rose oil (5 per cent in dilution) to a bowl of warm water and bathe the affected area.

Skin Treatments: Creams, Gels, Lotions, Masks and Oils

The proportions used for mixing skin creams, gels, masks and oils are the same as for massage purposes – *see page 42*. A basic non-allergenic cream recipe is as follows:

- 30 g melted beeswax
- 100 ml vegetable oil
  (to include 10 ml wheatgerm oil)
- 50 ml flower water (such as rosewater).

For skin care, carrier oils such as avocado, hazelnut, borage, peach and apricot kernel can also be included in the blend to suit different skin types. Nowadays, most commercial rosewater is unfortunately synthetic (addresses of suppliers of 100 per cent pure rosewater can be found at the end of the book).

Another method is to place 500 g of red rose petals in a saucepan together with 500 ml of boiling water. Cover with a tight-fitting lid and simmer for 30 minutes. Allow to cool. Strain into a glass bottle with a top or stopper and store ready for use.

Vaporization

There are many vaporizing methods available now — you can use a terracotta oil burner or an electric diffuser, or you can simply put a few drops of rose oil in a small bowl of hot water placed on a radiator or other heat source. This method is particularly useful for disinfecting a sick room, or simply for scenting a room in place of incense.

SAFETY DATA

Rose oil/absolute (Moroccan, Bulgarian, Turkish) is non-irritating, non-sensitizing and nonphototoxic to human skin. Rose is one of the safest oils, with low toxicity levels and no dermal contra-indications apart from one recorded case of sensitization (but this may have been caused by impurities in the absolute):

Rose absolute French was non-irritating and nonphototoxic, but it produces one sensitization reaction in 25 subjects tested.[1]

However, as a mild emmenagogue rose is best avoided (just to be on the safe side) during the first four months of pregnancy.

Babies, young children and women in the latter stages of pregnancy should take special care using all essential oils, because of their concentration. Despite the low toxicity levels of rose, it is advisable not to use it neat for treating children under 18 months of age – and always dilute for use during pregnancy.

Note: ESSENTIAL OILS SHOULD NOT BE TAKEN INTERNALLY!

STORAGE

For storage purposes rose oil/absolute should be kept in an air-tight dark glass container, away from light and heat and well out of the reach of children or pets. Unlike many essential oils (especially the citrus oils), rose improves with age and matures like a good wine!

Note: Pure rose oil can interact with certain plastics – plastic containers are therefore best avoided.

IT IS VERY IMPORTANT TO OBTAIN ROSE OIL FROM A REPUTABLE SOURCE TO ENSURE A SAFE AND EFFECTIVE THERAPEUTIC RESULT!

PART 2

A–Z of Health and Beauty Applications

acne/blemished skin; ageing/mature skin; amenorrhoea (absent periods); anorexia/loss of appetite; anxiety; asthma; blepharitis; bruises; children; cold sores; conjunctivitis/ophthalmia; cuts and wounds; depression; dermatitis and eczema; dry/cracked skin; dysmenorrhoea (painful periods); faintness and dizziness; haemorrhoids; hangover; hay fever; headaches; heat rash; high blood-pressure; immune system (to strengthen); infectious illness; insomnia; leucorrhoea and pruritis; menopausal problems; menorrhagia (heavy periods); menstruation problems; migraine; mouth ulcers; palpitations; perfume uses; perspiration (excessive); pregnancy and childbirth; premenstrual tension (PMT); scars; sensitive skin; sexual problems; skin care; stress; thread veins; varicose veins

Note: The instructions given in this section are for rose oil diluted to 5 per cent in a light carrier oil base (such as fractionated coconut oil or jojoba), unless otherwise stated.

ACNE/BLEMISHED SKIN

These unsightly skin conditions are caused by an overactivity of the sebaceous glands, and are especially common during adolescence, the menopause and at times of hormonal upheaval, such as before or during menstruation.

A very greasy, congested skin results in a rough surface texture, enlarged pores, spots, pimples and blackheads. The condition can be exacerbated further by poor diet, too little exercise, lack of hygiene, stress and other emotional factors. Scrupulous attention to hygiene prevents the condition from spreading.

Although rose oil is not the best choice for treating spots directly, it does have a soothing, healing and purifying effect on the skin as a whole. Rosewater is therefore a valuable ingredient when used in an antiseptic, astringent lotion for toning and cleansing the complexion:

• To make a toner/cleanser for blemished skin,
  mix together 25 ml witch-hazel, 75 ml rosewater,
  1 tbsp glycerine, 10 drops of lavender, 10 drops
  of geranium and 5 drops of bergamot (bergapten-

free). Shake well! Apply night and morning
before moisturizing.
• Make up a 0.5–1 per cent rose ointment by
adding 10–20 drops rose oil (5 per cent) to 1 tsp
of base cream or gel. Apply as a cleansing/mois-
turizing treatment for blemished or irritated skin.
See also Chapter 6, Skin Treatments.
• For an astringent and reviving cosmetic vinegar
to strengthen the acid mantle of the skin, mix
6 parts rosewater with 2 parts vinegar.
• Other measures: neat lavender or tea tree oil can
be used to treat individual spots night and morning using a cotton bud (cotton swab), as well as in
baths and for a facial steam.
  See also **Skin Care**

AGEING/MATURE SKIN
Cell division slows down as the body grows older
and the outer epidermis of the skin becomes thinner
and begins to lose its tone and suppleness. Ageing is
inevitable, but essential oils can do much to slow
down the effects by encouraging the skin cells to
regenerate. An oil such as rose can also help to keep
the skin healthy, lubricated and elastic, making it less
prone to wrinkles. General lifestyle is also, of
course, very important: smoking, drugs, a poor diet,
too much sun, central heating and stress can all speed
up the ageing process.

> *Rose hip seed oil, whose common name is Rosa Mosqueta, has been shown to be most effective in the field of tissue regeneration … wrinkling and dried skin was considerably attenuated and hydrated.*[1]

- Avoid soaps or alcohol-based products, which dehydrate the skin. Instead use a natural toner/cleanser twice daily: add 10 drops each of frankincense and lavender and 5 drops of neroli to 75 ml of rosewater, let this stand for up to a month, then filter. Add 25 ml glycerine and shake well.
- The regular use of a facial oil or cream containing cytophylactic oils (those that stimulate new cell growth and prevent wrinkles) is vital. A good basic blend for the face and neck is as follows: 50 ml jojoba (or almond oil) plus 1 tsp wheatgerm, 10 drops of lavender, 20 drops of rose (5 per cent in dilution), 3 drops neroli and 2 drops frankincense. An extra teaspoon of a rich carrier oil such as apricot kernel, avocado, hazelnut, evening primrose, peach kernel or especially rose hip seed oil may also be added. *See also Chapter 6, Skin Treatments.*
- To treat and help prevent wrinkles around the eyes, add 5 drops of rose (5 per cent) to 1 tsp wheatgerm oil (or rose hip seed oil) and apply gently to the area around the eyes before bed.
- Gentle massage, avoiding the delicate area around

the eyes, helps to improve the circulation and
muscle tone; use the following blend: 1 tbsp
jojoba (or sweet almond oil) with 15 drops of
rose oil (5 per cent).

- A face mask used once a week also helps rejuve-
nation. A basic mask can be made by mixing
2 tbsp clay, 2 tsp runny honey, 1 tsp water and
15 drops of rose oil (5 per cent).
- Other oils which help prevent ageing include:
lavender, neroli, frankincense, carrot seed, elemi,
galbanum, myrrh and patchouli.
See also **Skin Care**

AMENORRHOEA (ABSENT PERIODS)

The absence of menstruation, a scanty or missed
period is common at the onset of puberty or during
the menopause. However, apart from during pregnancy a woman's monthly cycle can cease to function
correctly as a result of emotional stress, shock, hormonal imbalance or a serious illness. Girls and
women suffering from anorexia nervosa also often
stop menstruating due to a lack of the nutrients
needed to synthesize the body's hormones.
Whatever the cause, the use of rose oil can help to
regulate and reassert a natural rhythm.

> *Rose ... is particularly valuable for women whose men-
> strual cycle is irregular and unpredictable, in helping to
> establish a predictable rhythm. This can be of great help*

> *to women who have been trying to conceive, as it makes it*
> *possible to predict the time of ovulation more accurately.*[2]

- Gently massage the abdomen with 30 drops of
  rose (5 per cent) in 1 tbsp carrier oil each day,
  especially during the few days prior to the onset.
- Use a few drops of rose oil in the bath regularly
  and in a massage or body oil – *see page 42* for
  preparing massage oils.
- Other oils of benefit: yarrow, clary sage, marjoram, myrrh (best used in combination). In addition, avoid stimulants like tea, coffee and alcohol
  – instead drink herbal teas, especially raspberry,
  yarrow and rose hip.

See also **Anorexia, Menopausal Problems**

ANOREXIA/LOSS OF APPETITE

Anorexia nervosa is characterized by an extreme loss
of appetite and often a complete aversion to food,
which results in dramatic weight loss. Most common
among teenage girls, this dangerous condition is
caused principally by psychological problems and
needs to be approached psychotherapeutically.
However, Patricia Davis and the French doctors
Mme Maury and Dr Lecleric all recommend rose
oil, especially for young anorexic girls, due to its
physically- and emotionally-enhancing properties.

> *Very often, an anorexic girl is afraid of growing up, and*
> *cannot come to terms with her own potential sexuality and*
> *having an adult woman's body. Rose oil cries out to be*
> *used here. It relates to woman's sexuality on every level,*
> *physical and emotional, and creates a wonderful feeling of*
> *being pampered, which is also a great help in restoring*
> *self-esteem.*[3]

- Use rose oil in baths, for massage, in vaporizers and as a perfume.
- Fennel, anise, mint and rose leaf/petal tea are also particularly valuable for this condition.

ANXIETY

Anxiety is one of the most common stress-related conditions encountered today, characterized by symptoms such as high blood-pressure, insomnia, palpitations or irritability. If the state of anxiety is allowed to persist over a prolonged period it can lead to secondary, more serious complaints such as stomach ulcers or heart failure. The regulating effect of rose on the vascular, digestive and nervous systems makes it particularly suitable for conditions of stress, which often start with anxiety or nervous tension and which can later lead to peptic ulcers, heart disease, and so on.

- Add 15–20 drops of rose oil (5 per cent) to a warm evening bath to relieve insomnia, restlessness, anxiety and nervous tension.

- Receiving a regular professional massage which incorporates a blend of suitable oils (such as rose, ylang ylang, lavender and neroli) can dramatically reduce anxiety levels.
- For self-treatment, blend 5–10 drops of rose (5 per cent) with 1 tsp sweet almond oil and massage into the hands and the soles of the feet.
- For a soothing room fragrance, use rose oil in a vaporizer or put a few drops on a hankie for inhalation throughout the day.
- Other measures: yoga, meditation and psychotherapy. Other essential oils of benefit: bergamot, neroli, ylang ylang, lavender.
  See also **Depression**, **High Blood-pressure**, **Insomnia**, **Stress**

ASTHMA

Asthma, characterized by wheezing and shortness of breath, commonly appears during early childhood and often ceases at puberty. It usually runs in families and, like many allergic conditions, an attack can be brought on by a number of different factors including diet, contact with allergens (such as dust, polish, hairspray or feathers), climatic conditions (especially damp), strenuous exercise and/or underlying emotional issues. Many things can be done to alleviate asthma once the cause of the attack and the pattern of the illness can be identified. As a relaxant and antispasmodic oil, rose (especially when combined with

massage) is very helpful for asthma. Used as a preventative measure it can inhibit attacks from occur-
ring so frequently. Research has shown that the spas-
molytic action of rose oil can protect against
bronchial asthma in guinea pigs.[4]

* Mix 15–30 drops of rose (5 per cent) with 1 tbsp
  sweet almond oil and massage the back in long
  sweeping movements, starting at the base of the
  spine, up over the shoulders, then down the sides
  of the body.
* Wear rose as a perfume, and use in vaporizers and
  in the bath at home as a general precautionary
  measure.
* Other oils of benefit: lavender, frankincense,
  geranium, chamomile.

BABIES
– *see* **Children**

BLEMISHED SKIN
– *see* **Acne**

BLEPHARITIS
This is a condition characterized by an inflammation
of the eyelids, giving the eyes a puffy appearance.

> *The petals of the Rose, and even its green leaves, are one*
> *of the best applications that can be had for weak or*

*inflamed eyes; while for a poultice they are always useful.
If our young folks would occasionally bathe their eyes in
an infusion of Rose leaves, either wild or cultivated, after
their weary studying over their lessons, the wearing of
spectacles would be a much less common sight than it is
now.*[5]

- A cotton pad soaked with rosewater makes an
  excellent soothing lotion when applied to the
  eyelids externally, as an alternative to the traditional poultice mentioned above.

Note: Neat essential oils should NEVER be brought
near or in contact with the eyes. The eyes are
extremely sensitive organs; only very minor eye
problems should be treated at home.

BRUISES

A bruise indicates that the tissue is damaged beneath
the skin's surface as a result of injury or pressure to
that area. Application with rose oil reduces inflammation, heals cell tissues and speeds up the healing
process.

*Bruises can be treated with a mixture of 30 drops of rose
oil and 10 ml jojoba oil … also a mixture of lavender and
rose in a ratio of 10:1 can be applied.*[6]

- Apply a cold compress of rosewater to ease
  inflammation, then dab a drop or two of rose oil
  (5 per cent) directly on to the affected area.

- Neat lavender or tea tree oil and arnica ointment are also very useful bruise remedies.

CHILDBIRTH
– *see* **Pregnancy and Childbirth**

CHILDREN
Due to its low toxicity level, rose is especially suited to the treatment of childhood complaints. Since most children like the smell of rose, it is also a good choice for regular bath times, massage or to vaporize in the bedroom. Babies and infants respond especially well to natural healing methods, but their extra sensitivity must be taken into account.

Do not attempt to substitute a home remedy for professional treatment if it is needed. Amounts used should correspond with the age of the child:

- Babies (0–12 months): 3 drops of rose (5 per cent) diluted in 1 tsp carrier oil for massage or bathing.
- Infants (1–5 years): 3–5 drops of rose (5 per cent) diluted in 1 tsp carrier oil for massage or bathing.
- Children (6–12 years): 10–15 drops of rose (5 per cent) for bathing, or diluted in 1 tbsp carrier oil for massage.
- Teenagers (over 12 years): use as for adults.
- Restlessness, hyperactivity and insomnia in babies, infants and older children can be helped

by the use of rose in the bath or for massage as directed above. Alternatively, use a vaporizer in the bedroom (ensure it is kept out of your child's reach).

• Chamomile and lavender are also very useful soothing children's remedies which can be used in combination with rose for a variety of common complaints including indigestion, teething pains and skin inflammations or rashes. Apply externally, always in dilution.

Note: ALL ESSENTIAL OILS SHOULD BE KEPT WELL OUT OF THE REACH OF CHILDREN.

COLDS
– *see* **Infectious Illness**

COLD SORES
A blister-like sore, usually found on the lips or face, caused by the virus *herpes simplex I*. The condition is infectious and can be spread to other parts of the body or to other people quite readily. Some people are particularly prone to cold sores, especially when they are run down or have been exposed to cold winds or hot sunshine.

The effect of rose/melissa oil (ratio of 1:2) on herpes zoster and herpes simplex can be confirmed. The oil is to be applied pure without dilution. An application of two or three times results in the disappearance of the complaints in one or two days.[7]

- Apply pure rose oil directly to the site of the problem – the presence of a base oil prevents this condition from healing.
- Tea tree (and to a lesser extent lavender oil) are also very effective remedies for herpes viruses, including chickenpox and shingles (*herpes zoster*) as well as genital herpes (*herpes simplex II*) – and are more economical to use, especially over larger areas of the body.

CONJUNCTIVITIS/OPHTHALMIA

Conjunctivitis is one of the most common eye infections. It is caused by an inflammation of the mucous membranes due to an allergy, bacteria, a virus or an external irritant. The eyes become red and sore and exude a yellowy-white sticky matter. In the morning the eyes may be 'glued' together.

- A cotton pad soaked with rosewater makes an excellent soothing, antiseptic lotion when applied to the eyelids externally.

Note: Neat essential oils should NEVER be brought near or in contact with the eyes. The eyes are extremely sensitive organs and only very minor eye problems should be treated at home.

CUTS AND WOUNDS

Rose is an excellent remedy for all types of skin abrasions but especially for slow-healing wounds or scars, due to its excellent antiseptic and cicatrizant properties. It also prevents scarring:

> *With rose ... the granulation of the skin and the healing of wounds is strongly accelerated...*[8]

- For open wounds, clean the cut or sore using rosewater, then apply neat lavender or tea tree oil.
- If the sore is slow to heal (and to prevent scarring), apply a few drops of rose oil in a 5 per cent dilution directly – not to be used on open wounds. Re-apply several times a day until the skin has healed completely.
  See also **Scars**

DEPRESSION

Depression can take many forms: it is often associated with a lack of energy and listlessness, but can also be accompanied by restlessness or agitation – sometimes alternating between the two. Rose has long been used to help alleviate depression due to its 'cephalic' or uplifting effect. A tonic to the heart, rose is also very beneficial for those coping with difficult life situations involving emotions such as grief, loss or fear.

- Add 15–20 drops of rose oil (5 per cent) to the bath – best used in combination with other anti-depressant oils, such as bergamot, jasmine and neroli.
- Receiving a regular professional massage using a blend of anti-depressant oils including rose can help encourage feelings of self-worth and well-being. Research has shown that the 'synergistic' combination of smell and touch can have a profoundly nourishing and comforting effect on the psyche.
- For an uplifting/soothing room fragrance use rose oil in a vaporizer; alternatively wear it as a perfume.
- Other measures: yoga, meditation and psychotherapy/ counselling. Other essential oils of benefit: bergamot, neroli, jasmine, melissa, lavender.

See also **Anxiety, Stress**

DERMATITIS AND ECZEMA

Dermatitis and eczema are general terms used to describe a variety of inflamed or irritated skin conditions, characterized by redness, flaky skin, rashes and itching, which in turn can lead to blisters, weepy sores and scabs. The cause of the problem can vary – though many forms of dermatitis are associated with hereditary allergic tendencies, especially to certain foods, notably dairy or wheat products. Another form, known as contact dermatitis, is the result of the skin's hypersensitivity to an external irritant such as a type of detergent or cosmetic, dust, wool, or some other substance. It is often very difficult to identify the cause, because the reaction may appear some time after the initial contact, or the skin may suddenly react to a familiar substance. In all cases, however, mental stress or other emotional factors tend to aggravate or trigger an attack.

Note: It may be necessary to experiment with different essential oils and types of treatment due to the individualistic nature of the problem.

- Make up a 0.5–1 per cent rose gel or non-oily cream by adding 10–20 drops of rose oil (5 per cent) to 1 tsp of a bland hypo-allergenic base gel or cream. Apply to the affected area twice daily.
- Add 15–20 drops of rose oil (5 per cent) to the bath water on a regular basis.
- Other measures: try to identify and remove possible causes of irritation; assess and improve the emotional environment if possible; the essential oils of chamomile, tea tree, melissa, lavender, neroli and bergamot (bergapten-free) are also beneficial for skin complaints of this type – either used individually or in combination.

    See also **Skin Care**

DIZZINESS
— *see* **Faintness and Dizziness**

DRY/CRACKED SKIN
Dry skin needs careful treatment, since this type of complexion is also the most 'brittle'. Dry skin becomes wrinkled more easily than greasy skin, and needs to be moisturized regularly, especially when exposed to the effects of central heating or too much sun. Very dry skin can become cracked and sore, especially on the hands and feet during the winter months. In severe cases it can be very painful, especially in association with frostbite or skin complaints such as psoriasis.

* Add 15 drops of rose oil (5 per cent) to 1 tbsp of jojoba or apricot kernel oil with 1 tsp of a rich oil such as avocado, borage, evening primrose, wheatgerm or rose hip seed oil. Apply every night as a moisturizer.
* A good toner/cleanser for dry skin can be made by adding 10 drops each of chamomile and lavender and 5 drops of sandalwood to 75 ml of rosewater. Allow this mixture to stand for up to a month, then filter. Add 25 ml glycerine and shake well. To be used twice daily.
* An excellent basic purifying and rejuvenating face mask for dry skin can be made by mixing 50 g of clay, 2 tsp cornflower, 1 egg yolk, 1 tsp evening

primrose oil or rose hip seed oil and 10 drops
of rose oil (5 per cent). Leave on the skin for
15 minutes, then rinse off with cool water.
- For cracked skin, mix 5 drops of rose oil (5 per
cent) with 1 tsp wheatgerm oil (or a thick moisturizing cream) and massage well into the affected
area night and morning. Continue until the condition improves. *See also Chapter 6, Skin Treatments.*
- Other measures: benzoin, myrrh, tea tree and
patchouli are also useful essential oils for cracked
skin used individually or in combination and
applied as directed above.

See also **Skin Care**

DYSMENORRHOEA (PAINFUL PERIODS)

Caused by uterine spasm during menstruation,
although the frequency and severity of period pains
is often also associated with diet and underlying
emotional factors. The soothing effect of rose combined with its excellent analgesic and antispasmodic
properties makes it an excellent remedy for period
pains (best used in combination with the other oils
mentioned below).

- Gently massage the abdomen and lower back with
30 drops of rose in 1 tbsp carrier oil.
- Hot compresses using a few drops of rose on a
flannel/face cloth (or a hot water bottle) placed
on the abdomen can help relieve pain.

- Relaxing in a hot rose bath eases pain and also soothes away stress and tension.
- Other oils of benefit: chamomile, clary sage, lavender, marjoram (best used in combination).

ECZEMA
– *see* **Dermatitis**

FAINTNESS AND DIZZINESS
Faintness or dizziness can result from a number of causes: severe shock, sunstroke, hangover, nervous exhaustion or very low blood-pressure. It is also common during the menopause and can be a symptom of PMT.

- Rosewater applied to the temples and face is reviving to the spirits and helpful in cases of emotional shock, nervous exhaustion, sunstroke, etc.
- Add 15–20 drops or rose oil (5 per cent) to the bath as a reviving 'pick-me-up' and to restore equilibrium.
- Simply inhaling rose by wearing it as a perfume can help counteract feelings of weakness, giddiness or nervous weakness.
  See also **Hangover, Menopause, Premenstrual Tension (PMT)**

FRIGIDITY
– *see* **Sexual Problems**

HAEMORRHOIDS

Haemorrhoids (or piles) are swollen veins in the walls of the anus; they can appear on the inside or outside. They may be itchy or painful and can bleed – surgery may be required in severe cases. A sedentary lifestyle, overweight, pregnancy, constipation and poor diet can all contribute to this condition. Rose oil helps soothe itching and encourages the dilated veins to return to normal due to its tonic and astringent action.

- Gently apply rose oil (5 per cent) directly to the site of the problem – use as required.
- Other measures: add a few drops of cypress oil to the bath water; the application of witch-hazel lotion is also an effective treatment for piles.
  See also **Varicose Veins**

HANGOVER

A rose petal bath was the traditional Roman remedy for hangover! As a cephalic and antispasmodic remedy, rose oil can help lift the spirits and ease headaches or faintness.

- Add 15–20 drops of rose oil (5 per cent) to the water for a deliciously scented morning bath. Afterwards, splash on a liberal amount of rosewater or apply rose oil as a perfume.
  See also **Faintness and Dizziness, Headaches**

HAY FEVER

Many people suffer from an allergic reaction to certain types of airborne pollen (or spores) which are released during the summer months. The eyes, throat and mucous membrane lining the nose are generally affected, resulting in sore or streaming eyes, headaches, sneezing and a blocked or runny nose. Rose oil is helpful for all types of allergic conditions, particularly because it is extremely mild on the skin. It is also specifically indicated for inflamed mucous membranes and can help soothe headaches. Rosewater is excellent to help soothe sore eyes.

Note: Experience has shown that often two or three oils (see those listed below) need to be alternated or combined to provide the greatest benefit for hay fever sufferers.

> *...a cream for dry mucous membranes in the nose (Bulgarian rose in eucerit) is very helpful.*[9]

- Wear rose as a perfume, or apply (with other oils) to a tissue for use throughout the day.
  Additionally, use in room vaporizers and baths.
- Regular massage with rose oil, especially in combination with chamomile and melissa can be very beneficial and help decrease the frequency or severity of an attack – see page 42 for how to make a massage oil.

- For sore, red eyes (or nose), apply cool compresses of rosewater (not the essential oil).
- Additional measures: Chamomile and melissa also help combat hayfever; a high intake of vitamin C can help control the severity of the attack; eating plenty of locally-produced honey (as then the bees will have fed on the pollen of surrounding vegetation) also acts as a prevention in some cases.

HEADACHES

Headaches can be caused by a number of different factors: sinus congestion, nervous stress, eye strain, too much sun or too much alcohol. Rose oil is especially good for nervous headaches and those associated with eye strain, sunstroke and hangovers.

> *Rose Vinegar, a specific on the Continent for headache caused by hot sun, is prepared by steeping dried rose petals in best distilled vinegar, which should not be boiled. Cloths or linen rags are soaked in the liquid and are then applied to the head.*[10]

- Inhale rose oil from a tissue, or apply rosewater to the temples or on a cold compress to the forehead or back of the neck.
- Headaches brought on by tension or stress can also be eased by a firm neck and shoulder massage using 3 drops of lavender and 5 drops of rose (5 per cent) in 1 tsp carrier oil.

- For eye strain, apply a cold compress of rosewater (not the essential oil) to the eyelids.
- Melissa and lavender oil are also valuable for nervous headaches.

See also **Hangover, Migraine, Stress**

HEAT RASH

Due to its excellent soothing, healing and analgesic properties, rose can provide instant relief from heat rash, red and sore skin – it can also prevent blistering. Research has also shown that rose oil is very effective used in an ointment for radiodermatitis or for skin that has been dried out or 'burned' by radiotherapy treatment (*see page 20*):

> *Hospital water with softeners added may cause dry skin but chamomile, rose, geranium and neroli all have a soothing effect when added to a base oil or calendula homoeopathic cream. Permission must always be obtained from the doctor prior to using anything on post radiotherapy skin.*[11]

- Make up an emollient cream to which 0.5–1 per cent of rose oil has been added – that is, 10–20 drops of rose oil (5 per cent) to 1 tsp cream. Apply very gently.
- For large areas, make up a lotion using 12 drops of lavender (or tea tree) oil in 1 tbsp of rosewater, shake well, then dab the area gently.

- Chamomile, lavender and tea tree are also valuable oils for heat rash and burns.

HERPES
– see **Cold Sores**

HIGH BLOOD-PRESSURE (HYPERTENSION)
Many people suffer from high blood-pressure these days, for it is a common side-effect of the fast pace of twentieth-century life. Stress, poor diet, too much alcohol and arteriosclerosis (the thickening and hardening of the arterial walls) can all contribute to this condition, which in the long term may lead to a serious kidney disease or heart failure. It is therefore vital to reduce blood-pressure levels as soon as possible: your diet, lifestyle, ambitions, etc. may need to be reassessed. Aromatherapy massage has also been found to be especially effective in implementing change in this way:

- If possible, put aside some time each week to have a regular professional massage, using a blend of relaxing oils including rose. Self-massage or massage between partners or friends is also valuable.
- Add 15–20 drops of rose oil (5 per cent) to the bath – or in combination with other relaxing oils such as ylang ylang, chamomile, marjoram or lavender.

- Use rose oil in a vaporizer at home or in the office on a regular basis – or use as a perfume for inhalation throughout the day.
- Other measures: yoga, meditation and psychotherapy/ counselling; reduce intake of stimulants including tea, coffee and alcohol. *See also* **Anxiety**, **Palpitations (Tachycardia)**, **Stress**

HYPERTENSION
– *see* **High Blood-pressure**

IMMUNE SYSTEM (TO STRENGTHEN):
Many essential oils, including rose (but particularly tea tree oil) stimulate the immune system and can assist the body in resisting as well as combating infection:

1 by directly opposing the threatening micro-organisms
2 by stimulating and increasing the activity of the organs and cells involved
3 by building up resistance and promoting the immune system as a whole.

People who use essential oils all the time, as part of their daily bathing, skin care and household routines, mostly have a high level of resistance to illness, 'catching' fewer colds etc. than average and recovering quickly if they do.[12]

- Use rose and other essential oils (particularly
  tea tree oil) for baths, massage and as room
  fragrances on an everyday basis.
- Other measures: a course of garlic capsules,
  vitamin E and vitamin C are also indicated.

IMPOTENCE
– *see* **Sexual Problems**

INFECTIOUS ILLNESS
Rose is a useful remedy to have at hand during an
infectious illness such as bronchitis or the common
cold, due to its ability to ease both physical and psychological discomfort, and because of its regulating
effect.

- Use rose in vaporizers throughout the duration
  of the illness, or add a few drops to a hankie
  for inhalation throughout the day and on a
  tissue beneath the pillow for nighttime, to aid
  relaxation.
- Other measures: tea tree, eucalyptus and rosemary are the best anti-infectious, expectorant and
  prophylactic agents, and can provide a 'first line
  of defence' against infectious illness; marjoram,
  lavender or chamomile oil can also be used in
  baths to soothe aching limbs and encourage restful sleep. In addition, take a course of garlic
  capsules and vitamin C tablets.

INSOMNIA

Sleeplessness is another common stress-related complaint which everyone suffers from at some time – whether it is before an exam, after an exhilarating experience, or simply due to an inability to switch off after a hard day's work.

- To encourage relaxation or a restful night (also excellent during pregnancy and for children), vaporize rose oil in the bedroom, or put a few drops on a tissue under the pillow. Sheets scented with rose oil also help induce sleep – but do not put rose oil directly on to bed linen as it can stain the fabric.
- Put 15–20 drops of rose oil (5 per cent) in a warm bath before retiring for the night, and relax for at least 10 minutes in the aromatic vapours.
- A regular professional aromatherapy massage using soothing oils such as rose is also very beneficial for reducing stress and inducing sleep – often before the session is finished!
- Other measures: chamomile or lavender oil make excellent sedatives when used as described for rose oil above; yoga and meditation; relaxant herbal teas.
- For more stubborn cases of insomnia valerian oil can be used in place of rose ... but do not use for more than two weeks at a stretch, as valerian has a powerful depressant effect on the whole central

nervous system.
See also **Stress**

LEUCORRHOEA AND PRURITIS

Leucorrhoea is an inflammation of the vagina caused by a proliferation of unwanted bacteria or fungi, which can have a variety of causes. Symptoms often include a thick white or yellow discharge and severe itching of the vaginal area.

Pruritis, or itching, is an irritating condition which generally accompanies any type of mild vaginal infection.

- As a sitz bath, add 12–18 drops of rose oil (5 per cent) to a bowl or shallow bath of warm water and soak for 5–10 minutes.
- Bathe daily, adding 15–20 drops of rose oil (5 per cent) to the bath water as a general antiseptic measure.
- Make up a 0.5–1 per cent rose ointment using a hypo-allergenic bland cream base. Add 10–20 drops of rose oil (5 per cent) to 1 tsp of the base cream. Apply to the affected area as required.
- In addition, avoid tight clothing, nylon underwear and harsh bubble baths; take garlic capsules and keep your consumption of tea, coffee, alcohol and spices to a minimum. Tea tree or lavender oils may also be used to treat mild vaginal infections in the same manner as rose.

MATURE SKIN
– see **Ageing Skin**

MENOPAUSAL PROBLEMS
Known as the 'change in life', the menopause is the time when menstruation ceases. It is frequently characterized by emotional and physical symptoms of ill-health such as headaches, hot flushes, depression, rapid mood swings, irritability and the tendency to put on weight. Due to its regulating and balancing effect, rose is particularly valuable in helping the body to adjust at this difficult time.

* Use rose oil (or lavender) in baths, vaporizers and for massage, according to specific symptoms.
  See also **Anxiety**, **Depression**, **Headaches**, **Leucorrhoea and Pruritis**, **Menstruation Problems**, **Migraine**, **Palpitations**, **Stress**

MENORRHAGIA (HEAVY PERIODS)
Sometimes menstrual flow can be excessive, often in association with cramps. Rose is helpful for menorrhagia due to its mild astringent action and strengthening effect on the uterus, and has a normalizing action on the female reproductive system as a whole.

> *Rose, indeed, can be beneficial for all kinds of menstrual problems, since it does not intrinsically reduce the flow or frequency, but has a regulating effect on the cycle, and is a uterine tonic.*[13]

- Gently massage the abdomen and lower back with 30 drops of rose in 1 tbsp carrier oil each day, especially during the few days prior to menstruation.
- Use 15–20 drops of rose oil (5 per cent) in the bath regularly and in a massage or body oil.
- Diet, lifestyle, exercise, etc. are also important factors to assess; raspberry leaf or rose petal tea can also help to strengthen the womb and normalize heavy periods.

MENSTRUATION PROBLEMS

Rose is a useful oil for all types of menstrual problems because of its regulating effect on the whole reproductive system. However, in all types of menstrual difficulty it is important to assess diet, exercise, stress and other factors which may be contributing to the condition.

For specific treatments see **Amenorrhoea (Absent Periods)**, **Dysmenorrhoea (Painful Periods)**, **Menorrhagia (Heavy Periods)** and **Premenstrual Tension (PMT)**.

MIGRAINE

Migraine is most commonly a food-related complaint, but an attack can also be triggered by an increase in stress or anxiety. Although aromatherapy is best used as a preventative measure by promoting relaxation as a part of one's everyday lifestyle, rose can also ease the pain and severity of an attack.

The fragrance of rose oil goes directly to the brain, and this direct access is important in the fighting of headaches and migraine... Even better is a mixture of oleum melissae officinalis (melissa oil) in equal parts with Bulgarian rose oil.[14]

- Apply a cold rosewater compress to the forehead or rub a little rose oil (5 per cent) onto the temples.
- As a preventative measure, use rose (or another soothing oil such as chamomile or lavender) on a daily basis in baths, vaporizers, for massage or as perfumes.

MOUTH ULCERS

Known as aphthous ulcers, these are tiny open sores which develop on the mucous membrane inside the mouth, on the tongue, gums, lips or cheeks. The centre is white with an inflamed red border which is sensitive to the touch. Their specific origin is unknown, although they may be caused by a mild viral infection or a sensitivity to certain foods. However, mouth ulcers only tend to appear when the body is run down or stressed.

- Apply rose oil (5 per cent in dilution) directly onto the ulcers with a cotton bud (cotton swab).
- Other measures: Tea tree oil is also an effective remedy for mouth ulcers used in the same man-

ner – but children especially do not like its taste. In addition, avoid alcohol and very spicy or acidic foods; drink plenty of water and eat fresh fruit and vegetables.

NERVOUS TENSION
– *see* **Stress**

PALPITATIONS (TACHYCARDIA)
This is a general term used to describe an irregular heartbeat, either 'missing a beat' or a rapid 'fluttering' of the heart. It can be brought on by exercise but is usually associated with high blood-pressure or stress. It is especially common during the menopause. Rose has a tonic yet soothing action on the heart and can help to alleviate palpitations arising from either a physical or emotional cause.

- Inhalations of rose can help calm a rapidly beating heart, although ylang ylang is recognized as the most useful oil for palpitations.
- Regular aromatic baths and massage using (individually or in combination) rose, ylang ylang, lavender, neroli, lavender or chamomile can also help to reduce stress levels and anxiety, which often trigger tachycardia.
  See also **High Blood-pressure**, **Menopause**, **Stress**

PERIODS (PAINFUL)
– see **Dysmenorrhoea**

PERFUME USES

The rose is queen of all perfumes ... and has been since the dawn of history! It is still found as a component in over 46 per cent of men's and 98 per cent of women's fragrances, and is considered indispensable for perfumery work ... there is even a saying, 'No perfume without rose!' Its warm, sweet floral scent with a faint piquant 'note' gives high-class perfumes a rich and distinctive quality. Rose is also an excellent fixing agent, for its scent is very long lasting. In short, rose oil imparts depth and body to virtually any blend, for it mixes well with almost everything:

> *'One day,' said the Persian poet Sadi, 'I saw a rose-bush surrounded by a tuft of grass. 'What!' I cried, 'does that vile plant dare to place itself in the company of Roses?'*
>
> *'I was about to tear the grass away when it meekly addressed me, saying: "Spare me! I am not the Rose, it is true; but from my perfume anyone can know at least that I have lived with Roses."'* [15]

Rose petals have a very tenacious scent which actually increases when they are kept (just as rose oil improves with age), which is why they form the basis for many pot pourris recipes. In Persia and

Damascus people used to bury jars of unopened rosebuds in the garden and dig them up on special occasions. The roses would open dramatically when exposed to warmth, suffusing the air with their fragrance. Lace bags of rose petals were also laid between sheets and clothes to protect them from moths and insects and infuse them with a lovely smell.

Rosewater also has a long-standing reputation as a perfume. In the Near East it plays a central role in many religious festivals, usually dispensed from a decanter made of dark blue glass. At New Year, for example, each guest is offered rosewater to wash and perfume the face and hands. At funerals it is also used in a similar ritual, to signify 'new life'. Rosewater is still used today to perfume mosques, and hospitality demands that a guest in an Islamic household be sprinkled with rosewater as soon as he or she arrives.

In the Hindu tradition, rose oil is frequently blended with sandalwood for ritual use – this perfume is called 'aytar'. In the West, rose oil (albeit in synthetic form) is the main ingredient in 75 per cent of all modern quality perfumes, such as the famous floral scent 'Red Rose' by Floris, which was first marketed in 1868. The simple handkerchief perfume 'Japanese Bouquet' contains the following ingredients, and may be re-created easily at home:

28 drops pure rose oil
16 drops cedarwood oil
16 drops patchouli oil
16 drops sandalwood oil
16 drops verbena (or bergamot) oil
8 drops vetiver oil

Alcohol may be added for dilution to the required strength.[16]

- Creating an individual perfume can be fun. Rose oil blends well with nearly all essential oils, especially sandalwood, cedarwood, lavender, patchouli, chamomile, clary sage, bergamot, geranium and other floral oils.
- Rose oil can be used neat as a perfume dabbed on the wrists or behind the ears (or diluted to 5 per cent in a base oil).
- Rosewater makes a refreshing, light perfume that can be splashed on more liberally than the concentrated oil.
- Rose petals and rose oil are traditionally used in pot pourris and were one of Tusser's original strewing herbs – *see page 41* for a pot pourris recipe.
- Rosewater can also be used to perfume linen, clothes, paper, leather or any other object – rose oil can cause staining.

PERSPIRATION (EXCESSIVE)

Rose oil or rosewater can be used as an excellent disinfectant and deodorant, having fresh, pleasing scents. Powdered rose petals were once used in place of talcum powder by the Romans.

- Splash rosewater beneath the arms or other areas which are prone to excessive perspiration in the morning/evening after bathing.
- Add 15–20 drops of rose oil (5 per cent) to a bowl of warm water and soak the feet for 5 minutes. Used in an evening bath, rose oil can help prevent night sweats.

PREGNANCY AND CHILDBIRTH

Using essential oils during pregnancy and to help with childbirth can be very beneficial in a variety of ways, because they operate on both a physiological and a psychological level. Rose is one of the most useful oils during pregnancy, not only because it is very safe but also because of its predominantly calming/healing/balancing character.

Because of the sensitivity of the growing child, however, all essential oils, including rose, should be used at only half the usual amount during pregnancy.

Note: Since rose is a mild emmenagogue, it is best avoided during the first four months of pregnancy.

In the field of obstetrics and paediatrics essential oils are being used on psychological, mental and physical levels. The reason for the great success of essential oils during pregnancy is that in this period women are intensely exposed to strong emotional ups and downs ... rose, cedar and clary sage are good remedies in these conditions when used in burners... Cooling refreshing compresses of rose-water can be used for general relief. Even puerperal depression can be relieved with essential oils such as grapefruit, bergamot, neroli, tangerine, rose, clary sage and vetiver.[17]

- An excellent oil to help prevent stretch marks can be made by blending 10 drops of rose (5 per cent) with 1 tbsp wheatgerm oil – use for light massage daily (after the fourth month) to the belly and breasts. This oil can also help to get rid of existing stretch marks. The mixture can also be rubbed into the perineum to help prepare for the birth.
- Aromatic bathing is a great pleasure and relief, especially towards the end of pregnancy. Add 10 drops of rose (5 per cent) to the bath, and relax in the aromatic vapours.
- A gentle massage using rose (in dilution) can be very enjoyable during the final stages pregnancy, and can help with a wide variety of problems such as backpain, anxiety or fatigue.
- During the birth, and in preparing to bring the baby back home, the use of vaporized oils (such

as rose or lavender) to scent the environment can be very conducive to creating an uplifting, relaxed mood. They also prevent the spread of airborne bacteria.

- To help heal the perineum after the birth, add a few drops of rose (or lavender) to a shallow bath, and soak. In addition, apply rose oil (5 per cent in dilution) directly to the perineum (unless there is an open cut). Repeat each day.
- Mastitis or engorged breasts can be eased by applying a warm rose and geranium compress, or by gently massaging with a rose and geranium ointment in a non-allergenic base – 15 drops of rose oil (5 per cent) and 3 drops of geranium to 1 tbsp cream or base oil.
- Postnatal depression can be helped by the use of rose in burners, baths and for general massage.

Note: Some essential oils should be avoided altogether during pregnancy, including basil, clove, cinnamon leaf, hyssop, juniper, marjoram, myrrh, sage and thyme. The following oils are best avoided during the first four months of pregnancy: fennel, peppermint and rosemary.

PREMENSTRUAL TENSION (PMT)

The symptoms of PMT are various: on a physical level they may include fluid retention, tender breasts, headaches, nausea or a swollen abdomen; on an emotional level symptoms commonly include depression, sudden mood swings, weepiness or unpredictable behaviour. Considering the overall 'harmonizing' effect of rose on the whole system, it is a very useful aid for women who suffer from PMT, both physically and emotionally.

- Use rose in baths and in a vaporizer during the ten days prior to menstruation, and throughout the duration of the period.
- A regular massage treatment with rose (and/or lavender, geranium or chamomile, individually or in combination) can be very helpful. For self-treatment, mix 30 drops of rose oil (5 per cent) in 1 tbsp light carrier oil, such as grapeseed, and apply gently to the abdomen and lower back.
- A nutritional approach to PMT has been developed over the past few years with excellent results. Supplements of evening primrose oil, vitamin B_6 and the B complex vitamins have also proved invaluable.

PRURITIS (ITCHING)
– *see* **Leucorrhoea/Pruritis**

SCARS
Rose oil (particularly when combined with rose hip seed oil) is very beneficial for the treatment of all types of scars including pigmented scars, stretch marks and scars caused by injury or surgery:

*Recent studies show that Rose Hip Seed Oil has a very
high percentage of linoleic acid (40 per cent) and
linolenic acid (39 per cent)... In trials, 26 per cent was
added to a cream base. These trials have been conducted
on multiple erytheme, acne scars, cheloids and surgical
scars. Excellent results were obtained, except for acne,
where the emollient character of the rose hip seed oil con-
tributed to blocking the patient's pores.*[18]

- Make up a ointment by adding 1 tsp of rose hip
  seed oil to 1 tsp of a hypo-allergenic cream base,
  together with 20 drops of rose oil (5 per cent).
  Apply at least twice daily.
- Palmarosa, neroli, lavender and frankincense oil
  can also help regenerate healthy tissue and
  remove scars.

SENSITIVE SKIN

If you have sensitive skin it is important to avoid all
possible irritants (such as lanolin- or alcohol-based
toiletries) and to use only the most gentle essences —
rose, chamomile, lavender, jasmine and neroli are
the best choices.

- Avoid harsh soaps or products which dehydrate
  the skin. Instead use a natural toner/cleanser
  twice daily: add 10 drops each of rose and lavender and 5 drops of chamomile to 75 ml of rosewater, let stand for up to a month and then filter.

Then add 25 ml glycerine and shake well.
- For moisturizing the skin, add 10 drops of rose
  (5 per cent) to 1 tsp of jojoba, apricot or peach
  kernel oil or to an anti-allergenic cream or lotion
  for daily use. *See also Chapter 6, Skin Treatments.*
  See also **Skin Care**

SEXUAL PROBLEMS

Many sexual problems such as frigidity or impotence
have a psychological basis and may be accompanied
by depression, anxiety or other stress-related conditions. The 'feel-good' effect of essential oils can do
much to alleviate these underlying factors, although
many essential oils (including rose), are also reputed
aphrodisiacs. In Chinese medicine, rose oil is used to
improve the virility of men and increase their sperm
count, while in Turkey a rose jam called 'gul' is used
as a sexual stimulant. Rose also features in a great
number of erotic elixirs or perfumes used in the
Orient and Near East.

In the West, the rose has always tended to be associated with the female sex — and with love. On a
physical level, the use of rose oil can help to regulate
a woman's menstrual cycle, making it easier for her
to conceive. On a more psychological level, rose oil
(particularly rose maroc) can help women suffering
from frigidity or sexual insecurity:

> *In my experience, this is a very valuable oil for any woman
> who is not secure in her own sexuality, whether her inse-
> curity is expressed as a lack of confidence in her own desir-
> ability, reluctance to acknowledge herself as a sexually
> mature person (for example, in cases of anorexia) or diffi-
> culties within an established relationship.* [19]

- Simply wear the oil as a perfume to create a sensual mood.
- Make a massage oil using rose, sandalwood and ylang ylang in a light base oil – *see instructions page 42*. Massage can be a very intimate experience and a means of enhancing sexual communication between you and your partner.
- As a bath oil or vaporized oil, rose creates a warm, romantic atmosphere. Set the scene for seduction or light a candle and simply enjoy the erotic aroma!

Note: Essential oils should not be allowed to come in contact with condoms as they can have a detrimental effect on the rubber.

SKIN CARE

The condition of the skin expresses the overall health of an individual. A relaxed attitude together with a well-balanced diet, enough exercise and a daily intake of plenty of spring water or herbal tea all help to keep the system in top condition. A stressful lifestyle, on the other hand, and too much coffee, tea and alcohol all take their toll on the skin, which can start to look dull and lifeless.

The appearance of the skin also depends on the type of skin care routine adopted. Products containing mineral oil or lanolin are not absorbed into the lower dermal layers where the newly emerging cells require optimum nourishment. Alcohol-based products dehydrate the skin and can cause irritation, as can many other synthetic ingredients. In contrast, natural vegetable oils, waxes and creams, together with specially selected essential oils, are ideal cosmetic aids because they are highly penetrative and can reach the small blood capillaries in the deeper dermal layers, thus rejuvenating the skin 'from within'.

Rose is one of the most useful skin care oils because, although it has good antiseptic properties, it is very mild on the skin. It is also an excellent cicatrizant (wound-healing) oil, promoting tissue or cell regeneration and preventing scarring. It is these properties which make it a valuable oil for the treatment of a wide range of specific skin conditions.

Rose oil and rosewater have been used as ingredients in cosmetics for centuries, and their effects have been well tried and tested. They are suited to all types of complexion, particularly dry, sensitive and ageing/mature skin. Together with rose hip seed oil, it is also one of the most effective oils for the treatment of scars and stretch marks. Different skin types require individual treatment, but a good basic skin care routine is as follows:

Every night:
- Remove make-up (if worn) using a light oil or bland cream.
- Cleanse face and neck using a toner/cleanser suited to your skin type.
- Apply moisturizer or night cream suited to your skin type.
- Apply moisturizing eye cream, lotion or gel.
- At least once a week use a mask made from natural ingredients (*see* **Ageing/Mature Skin**).

Every morning:
- Wipe face and neck with toner/cleanser suited to skin type.
- Apply moisturizer, then make-up (if worn).
  For the treatment of specific skin types see
  Acne/Blemished Skin, Ageing/Mature Skin, Dermatitis and Eczema, Dry/Cracked Skin, Scars, Sensitive Skin and **Thread Veins**.

STRESS

Stress is not a illness as such, but a 'multi-dimensional syndrome' which can cause a wide range of physical ailments and psychological problems ranging from high blood-pressure, headaches or digestive complaints to feelings of constant tiredness, depression or nervous anxiety. Stress also weakens the immune system and, in the long term, makes an individual more susceptible to all kinds of disease.

Recent research indicates that stress is most probably a causative factor or a trigger for many of our so-called 'civilization' diseases such as cancer, ME, stroke, and HIV. Material proof of the widespread sense of 'dis-ease' experienced today is shown by the high consumption of tranquillizers and stimulants, although it is well known that addiction, toxicosis and other side-effects can be caused by these products if taken regularly. Any treatment which can help to de-stress or revitalize the organism without producing detrimental side-effects is therefore of great value.

> *The possibility of applying new therapies to these widespread psycho-neuroses is therefore of considerable importance … essential oils that are employed in aromatherapy, in the appropriate doses, are harmless to the organism and do not cause troubles like those produced by the ordinary psychological drugs. Very conclusive experiments in this direction have been carried out in various clinics for nervous diseases, on patients affected by hysteria or psychic depression.*[20]

Stress-related problems are an area in which aromatherapy enjoys a great deal of success, due to the powerful restorative benefits of the combination of touch and smell. During a massage the essential oils themselves also interact and de-stress the body in two ways: through inhalation (primarily psychological effects) and through dermal absorption (primarily physiological effects). By easing the problem at its source, rather than by treating just the symptoms, aromatherapy is especially valuable for those who suffer from a number of different responses to stress simultaneously.

- For immediate self-treatment make a massage oil using 5 drops of rose oil (5 per cent) in 1 tsp almond oil and rub gently into the solar plexus, back of the neck and temples.
- Use rose oil in baths, vaporizers, massage, perfumes, etc. on a regular basis. The effect of the fragrance alone helps soothe nervous tension and irritability and helps sufferers overcome emotional stress – especially 'problems of the heart' such as grief, anger, jealousy and shock.
- Other measures: professional help may be required in the form of massage, psychotherapy, etc. in order to get at the root of the problem. *For specific symptoms see* **Anxiety**, **Depression**, **Faintness**, **High Blood-pressure**, **Insomnia** and **Palpitations**.

THREAD VEINS

These are caused by a circulatory problem and make the capillary walls dilate or stretch, resulting in fine red lines beneath the skin of the cheeks, giving the face a ruddy appearance. The problem mainly affects those with a fair, delicate or sensitive complexion, though it can also be a sign of ageing. Rose is a remarkable ally in the fight against thread veins or 'broken' capillaries due to its tonic and astringent effect – but it does require perseverance.

- Apply soothing compresses of rosewater to the cheeks. Mix together 1 tbsp of rose hip seed oil (or a hypo-allergenic cream) and 30 drops of rose oil: gently massage into the affected area twice daily.
- Other measures: chamomile and carrot seed oil are also beneficial for this condition; avoid exposure to harsh sunlight and extremes of heat or cold; consumption of alcohol, coffee and tea should be kept to a minimum.

VARICOSE VEINS

These are the result of poor circulation and inadequate elasticity in the walls of the veins, usually in the legs. The veins become swollen and congested so the blood does not flow back to the heart. Lack of exercise, standing for long periods, overweight, pregnancy and poor nutrition all contribute to this condition. Cypress and rose oils can do much to tone the blood vessels and reduce dilation, although successful treatment does require perseverance.

- Make up a massage oil or cream containing rosé and cypress oils and rub gently into the area around and above the veins. DO NOT press directly on them or below them, and work up the legs towards the heart. The legs should be elevated after massage. Repeat daily. *See page 42* for instructions on how to make effective massage oils/creams.
- Other measures: gentle exercise such as swimming or yoga (especially inverted postures); general massage or warm (not hot) baths with circulatory stimulants such as rosemary or juniper oils can help improve the circulatory system as a whole; when possible rest the legs higher than the head; take a course of garlic capsules.

WRINKLES
– see **Ageing/Mature Skin**

Different Types
of Rose Species

All roses are members of the *Rosaceae* family, a large botanical genus (or family) which has expanded rapidly over the last century due to the popular hybridization of cultivated roses. Experimentation with new rose species is also continually being carried out with regard to the highly scented roses which may be used specifically for the production of essential oils. However, there are several types, apart from those mentioned in the main body of this book, which have played a steady if relatively minor role in the essential oil and perfumery industry over the years.

Dog Rose (R. canina)
The 'Dog Rose' is the common, wild rose found in Britain and other parts of Europe. Its name is thought to have derived from the term 'dagger' or 'dag' rose, so called because of its long, sharp thorns. A deciduous, rambling shrub, it can reach

3 m (10 ft) in length and bears delicate pink or white single five-petalled flowers. The leaves and especially the hips were once a common European folk remedy. The flowers are still occasionally employed in the production of an essential oil. Like the Gallic and the Damask Rose, the Dog Rose is an extremely variable species. It is the national flower of England.

Musk Rose (R. moscatta)

The Musk Rose is a snow white rose with a very fragrant scent. It matures into a vigorous bushy shrub; in Bulgaria it is often grown as a wind-break or hedge between the more refined Damask Rose plants. It is used in Bulgaria to produce an essential oil, though inferior in quality to the oil that comes from the Damask Rose.

White Rose (Rosa x alba)

The Alba Roses are an ancient group, hybrids between the Dog Rose and a Gallic or Damask variety. Alba roses are always white or pale pink with sweetly scented flowers and bluish leaves. They make large bushes bearing few thorns. The main cultivar of the White Rose used for essential oil production is called 'Semiplena'.

Tea Rose (R. indica)

The essential oil from the Oriental or Tea Rose is mainly produced in the East where it is used as a perfume and remedy. Tea roses are generally either climbers or small, sparse bushes bearing a continuous succession of large, beautiful flowers in shades of pink, buff or light yellow.

Japanese Rose (R. rugosa)

This variety is characterized by large, simple red Bordeaux petals and has a 'classic' rose scent. Like the Chinese Rose (*R. chinensis*) it has the advantage of being a perpetual-flowering type, which means the harvest does not need to be limited to one short period in the year. The essential oil contains 81 per cent alcohols (phenylethanol: 53 per cent; geraniol: 5.6 per cent; citronellol: 16.8 per cent) which gives it a warm, soft, honey-like perfume.

Comparative Constituents
of Rose Oil

The chemical composition of rose oil is extremely
complicated due to the number of constituents
involved, and especially the amount of trace ele-
ments present.

> It is normal that the 'mystical and magic' rose, due to its
> perfectly divine perfume, was the first to become the object
> of numerous classical analyses ... at the turn of this cen-
> tury, only eight constitutionally defined substances had
> been discovered in rose essence ... from the start of the six-
> ties, modern analytical techniques resulted in an acceler-
> ation in the volatile components: 200 by 1970 and 400
> by 1990.[1]

The classic 'old' varieties of roses contain between
35 per cent and 85 per cent essential alcohols such as
phenylethanol, citronellol, nerol and geraniol, and
these play important roles in creating the 'classic'
rose scent. Although it is generally agreed that about

82 to 88 per cent of the constituents of most rose oils or absolutes are covered by only about half a dozen main components (see below), it is the other small percentage which can dramatically effect the fragrance and quality of a product. For example, the compound mainly responsible for the 'honey-note' in R. *damascena* has been shown to be 'damascenone', comprising only 0.1 per cent of the oil.

This means that different varieties of rose, and even different cultivars if the same species, can produce products with quite diverse characteristics and compositions. The Gallic Rose (*R. gallica*), for example, contains a relatively low percentage of alcohols (about 47.5 per cent) compared to R. *damascena* and R. *centifolia*. The following table compares the main components of Bulgarian rose oil (*R. damascena*) or 'attar' (which is similar in composition to the Turkish oil) to French rose absolute (*R. centifolia*):

	R. damascena	R. centifolia
citronellol	34–55%	18–22%
phenylethanol	1.5–3%	c. 63%
geraniol and nerol	30–40%	10–15%
farnesol	0.2–2%	0.2–2%
stearopten	16–22%	c. 8%

plus traces of: nonanon, linalool, nonanal, phehylacetaldehyde, citral, carvone, citronellyl acetate, 2-phenylmethyl acetate, eugenol, rose oxide.[2]

For an extensive and more detailed picture of the components of rose oil, see 'Composition of Essential Oils, Part 7: Bulgarian Oil of Rose (*R. Damascena*)' by E. Kovat, *Journal of Chromatography* (1987), Elsevier Science Publishers B.V. Amsterdam.

References

Introduction

1. G. Rose and P. King, *The Love of Roses* (Quiller Press, 1990), p.49.

Chapter 1

1. J. Lawless, *Aromatherapy and the Mind* (Thorsons, 1994), p.201.
2. D. Ackerman, *A Natural History of the Senses* (Chapmans, 1990), p.36.
3. E.Kiaer, *Methuen Handbook of Roses* (Methuen, 1966), p.14.
4. Ibid.
5. Rose and King, *The Love of Roses*, p.111.
6. J. E. Cirlot, *A Dictionary of Symbols* (Routledge & Kegan Paul, 1962), p.275.

Chapter 2

1. Cited in R. Tisserand, *The Art of Aromatherapy* (C. W. Daniel, 1979), p.274.
2. Ibid.
3. Dr W. S. Brud and Dr I. Szydlowska, 'Bulgarian Rose Oil', *The International Journal of Aromatherapy* 3 (3), 1991, p. 18.
4. Ibid.
5. N. Culpeper, *Culpeper's Complete Herbal* (W. Foulsham, 1952), p.298.
6. R. Lovell, *A Compleat Herball* (2nd edn, 1666), p. 369.

Chapter 3

1. E. Launert, *Edible and Medicinal Plants* (Hamlyn, 1981), p.74.
2. *British Herbal Pharmacopoeia* (British Herbal Medicine Association, 1983), p.180.

3. Review by Kirov and Vankov which summarized some of the results of research, in the journal *Medico-Biologic Information* (1988), as reported in Dr W. S. Brud and Dr I. Szydlowska, 'Bulgarian Rose Oil', *The International Journal of Aromatherapy* 3 (3), 1991, pp.18–19.

4. D. Wabner and I. Wurdack, 'Rose Oil: Its Use in Therapy and Cosmetics', *The International Journal of Aromatherapy* 1 (4), 1989, p.28.

5. Ibid.

6. R. M. Gattefossé, *Gattefossé's Aromatherapy* (C. W. Daniel, 1993), p.69.

7. M. Maury, *Marguérite Maury's Guide to Aromatherapy – The Secret of Life and Youth* (C. W. Daniel, 1989), p.86.

8. M. Maury, *Guide to Aromatherapy*, p.87.

9. T. Tachev, *Folia Medica* 11 (1969), p.307, as cited in Dr W. S. Brud and Dr I. Szydlowska, 'Bulgarian Rose Oil', *The International Journal of Aromatherapy* 3 (3), 1991, p.18.

Chapter 4

1. M. Billot, the famous French perfumer, cited in Dr W. S. Brud and Dr I. Szydlowska, 'Bulgarian Rose Oil', *The International Journal of Aromatherapy* 3 (3), 1991, pp.18–19.

2. From document in National Library of Paris, cited in W. A. Poucher, *Perfumes, Cosmetics and Soaps* (vol. II, Chapman and Hall, 1932), p.167.

Chapter 5

1. D. Wabner and I. Wurdack, 'Rose Oil: Its Use in Therapy and Cosmetics', *The International Journal of Aromatherapy* 1 (4), 1989, p.29.

2. R. Tisserand, *The Art of Aromatherapy* (C. W. Daniel, 1979), p.275.

3. P. Davis, *Subtle Aromatherapy* (C. W. Daniel, 1991), p.219.

Chapter 6

1. A. Y. Leung, *Encyclopedia of Common Natural Ingredients* (Wiley, 1980), p.280.

A – Z

1. J. Kusmirek, 'The Basics of Base Oils', *Aromatherapy Quarterly* 33, 1992, p.9.
2. P. Davis, *Aromatherapy: An A – Z* (C. W. Daniel, 1988), p.224.
3. Davis, *A – Z*, p.27.
4. D. Wabner and I. Wurdack, 'Rose Oil: Its Use in Therapy and Cosmetics', *The International Journal of Aromatherapy* 1 (4), 1989, p.28.
5. D. Younger, *Household Gods* (E. W. Allen, 1898), p.64.
6. Wabner and Wurdack, 'Rose Oil', p.29.
7. Ibid.
8. Ibid.
9. Ibid.
10. M. Grieve, *A Modern Herbal* (Penguin, 1931), p.688.
11. C. Horrigan RNT, 'Complementing Cancer Care III', *The International Journal of Aromatherapy* (2), 1992, p.28.
12. Davis, *A–Z*, p.173.
13. Davis, *A–Z*, p.224.
14. Wabner and Wurdack, 'Rose Oil', p.29.
15. C. Powell, *The Meaning of Flowers* (Jupiter Books, 1977), p.119.
16. N. Groom, *The Perfume Handbook* (Chapman & Hall, 1992), p.317.
17. S. Fischer-Rizzi, 'Dedicated to Better Birth', *The International Journal of Aromatherapy* 4 (1), 1992, p.10.
18. Kusmirek, 'The Basics', p.9.
19. Davis, *A – Z*, p.290.
20. Rovesti, cited in R. Tisserand, *The Art of Aromatherapy* (C. W. Daniel, 1979), p.98.

Appendix B

1. R. Teranishi, R. G. Buttery and H. Sugisawa, 'Volatile Constituents of Roses', *Bioactive Volatile Compounds from Plants*, (American Chemical Society, 1993), p.269.
2. D. Wabner and I. Wurdack, 'Rose Oil: Its Use in Therapy and Cosmetics', *The International Journal of Aromatherapy* 1 (4), 1989, p.30.

Bibliography

D. Ackerman, *A Natural History of the Senses* (Chapmans, 1990)

A. M. Aldous, 'The Rose and the Apothecary', *The Rose Annual* 5, 1950

Aqua Oleum, *The Essential Oil Catalogue* (Aqua Oleum, 1994)

A. Attila and A. Bayrak, 'Volatile Oil Composition of Turkish Rose', *Journal Sci. Food Agric.* 64, 1994

K. H. C. Baser, 'Turkish Rose Oil', *Perfumer & Flavorist* 17, 1992

British Herbal Pharmacopoeia (British Herbal Medicine Association, 1983)

Dr W. S. Brud and Dr I. Szydlowska, 'Bulgarian Rose Oil', *The International Journal of Aromatherapy* 3 (3), 1991

J. E. Cirlot, *A Dictionary of Symbols* (Routledge & Kegan Paul, 1962)

N. Culpeper, *Culpeper's Complete Herbal* (W. Foulsham, 1952)

P. Davis, *Aromatherapy: An A – Z* (C. W. Daniel, 1988)

—, *Subtle Aromatherapy* (C. W. Daniel, 1991)

I. Day, *Perfumery with Herbs* (Darton, Longman & Todd, 1979)

H. Edland, *The Pocket Encyclopaedia of Roses* (Blandford Press, 1963)

S. Fischer-Rizzi, 'Dedicated to Better Birth', *The International Journal of Aromatherapy* 4 (1), 1992

R. M. Gattefossé, *Gattefossé's Aromatherapy* (C. W. Daniel, 1993)

R. Genders, *Natural Beauty* (Webb & Bower, 1986)

M. Gibson, *The Book of the Rose* (Macdonald General Books, 1980)

M. Grieve, *A Modern Herbal* (Penguin, 1931)

N. Groom, *The Perfume Handbook* (Chapman & Hall, 1992)

E. Guenther, *The Essential Oils* (New York: Van Nostrand, 1948)

J. Hériteau, *Potpourris and Other Fragrant Delights* (Penguin, 1978)

M. Hillier, *Roses: The Little Scented Library* (Dorling Kindersley, 1991)

C. Horrigan, 'Complementing Cancer Care', *The International Journal of Aromatherapy* 4 (2), 1992

E. Keller, *Aromatherapy Handbook for Beauty, Hair and Skin Care* (Rochester, VT: Healing Arts Press, 1991)

E. Kiaer, *Methuen Handbook of Roses* (Methuen, 1966)

J. Kusmirek, 'The Basics of Base Oils', *Aromatherapy Quarterly* 33, 1992

E. Launert, *Edible and Medicinal Plants* (Hamlyn, 1981)

J. Lawless, *The Encyclopaedia of Essential Oils* (Element Books, 1992)

—, *Home Aromatherapy* (Kyle Cathie, 1993)

—, *Aromatherapy and the Mind* (Thorsons, 1994)

—, *Lavender Oil* (Thorsons, 1994)

—, *Tea Tree Oil* (Thorsons, 1994)

Dr B. M. Lawrence, 'Progress in Essential Oils' *Perfumer & Flavorist* 16, 1991

A. Y. Leung, *Encyclopedia of Common Natural Ingredients* (Wiley, 1980)

R. Lovell, *A Compleat Herball* (2nd edn, 1666)

L. Manniche, *An Ancient Egyptian Herbal* (British Museum Publications, 1989)

M. Maury, *Marguérite Maury's Guide to Aromatherapy – The Secret of Life and Youth* (C. W. Daniel, 1989)

M. Mességué, *Health Secrets of Plants and Herbs* (Pan, 1979)

R. A. and I. Miller, *The Magical and Ritual Use of Perfumes* (Destiny Books, 1990)

Y. R. Naves and Mazuyer, *Natural Perfume Materials* (New York: Reinhold, 1947)

P. Ody, *Complete Medicinal Herbal* (Dorling Kindersley, 1993)

R. Phillips, *Wild Flowers of Britain* (Pan, 1977)

R. Phillips and M. Rix, *Roses* (Pan, 1988)

W. A. Poucher, *Perfumes, Cosmetics and Soaps* (vol. II, Chapman and Hall, 1932)

C. Powell, *The Meaning of Flowers* (Jupiter Books, 1977)

J. Ramsbottom, *A Book of Roses* (Penguin, 1939)

G. Rose and P. King, *The Love of Roses* (Quiller Press, 1990)

D. Ryman, *Aromatherapy* (Piatkus, 1991)

J. Seymour, *Roses* (Colour Library International, 1978)

R. E. Shepherd, *History of the Rose* (Macmillan, 1954)

R. Teranishi, R. G. Buttery and H. Sugisawa, 'Volatile Constituents of Roses', *Bioactive Volatile Compounds from Plants* (American Chemical Society, 1993)

G. S. Thomas, *The Rose Book* (John Murray, 1994)

R. Tisserand, *The Art of Aromatherapy* (C. W. Daniel, 1979)

Dr J. Valnet, *The Practice of Aromatherapy* (C. W. Daniel, 1980)

C. Vuilleumier, I. Flament and P. Sauegrain, 'Headspace Measurement of Evaporation rates of Perfumes Applied to the Skin: Application to Rose Essential Oils and Their Principle Components' *Perfumer & Flavorist* 20, 1995

D. Wabner, 'On the Scent of a Real Rose', *The Herbal Review* Winter 1988

—, 'Discovering the Magic of Rose Oil', *The Herbal Review* Autumn 1989

D. Wabner and I. Wurdack, 'Rose Oil: Its Use in Therapy and Cosmetics', *The International Journal of Aromatherapy* 1 (4), 1989

D. Warren-Davis, 'The Symbolism of the Rose', *The Herbal Review* Autumn 1989

Dr P. Wilde and J. Grayson, 'Rose and Crown', *Royal Horticultural Society* Nov. 1993: 504

Dr P. Wilde and S. Whitton, 'Wild about the Rose', *Aromatherapy Quarterly* 38, 1993

R. C. Wren, *Potter's New Cyclopaedia of Botanical Drugs and Preparations* (C. W. Daniel, 1985)

D. Younger, *Household Gods* (E. W. Allen, 1898)

Useful Addresses

It is advisable always to buy rose oil from a reputable supplier, to ensure that it is of the highest quality so as to achieve maximum therapeutic results. Aqua Oleum have many years of experience in the field and provide a wide range of top-quality essential oils, including rose oil, at very competitive prices. They can be purchased from health and wholefood stores, as well as from some chemists, throughout the UK. Mail-order items, carrier oils, burners, individually formulated products and further information can be obtained from:

Aqua Oleum
Unit 3
Lower Wharf
Wallbridge
Stroud
Glos GL5 3JA
UK
Tel: 01453 753 555

Aqua Oleum also supply rose oil internationally to the following countries:

Eire

Wholefoods Wholesale	Soap Opera Ltd
Unit 2D	Unit 3 Enterprise Centre
Kylemore Industrial Estate	Stafford Street
Dublin 10	Nenagh
	Co. Tipperary

USA and Canada

Natura Trading Ltd.
4454 West 10th Avenue
Vancouver, British Columbia
V6R 2H9

Japan

Raiko Co. Ltd
4B, 2-2-8 Roppongi Minato-Ku
Tokyo

Kawahito Trading Office
Room 308 Fushu Musashino
High Raise 3-11-13
Sakae-cho
Fushu-shi
Tokyo 183

Hong Kong

The New Age Shop
7 Old Bailey Street
Central
Taiwan

Ecole Internationale D'Esthétique
D'Europe
15F 1 547 Kwang Fiu South Road
Hsin Vi Zone
Taipei

Norway

Terapi Consult AS
Frysjaveien 27
0883 Oslo

Denmark and Sweden

Urtekram A/S
Klostermarken 20
DK-9550 Mariager
Denmark

Finland

Luonnonruokatukku Aduki Ky
Kirvesmiehenkatu 10
00810 Helsinki

Index